PENGUIN

THREE TRUTHS OF WELL BEING

Sadhguru is a yogi, mystic and prominent spiritual leader of our times. He is the founder of the Isha Foundation in Coimbatore, a spiritual movement that offers a system of powerful and ancient yogic practices for the modern person.

PRAISE FOR THE BOOK

'Sadhguru's book is an exemplary piece of work. It takes the reader through the intricate journey of discovering the real key to well-being in the most simplified manner. A must-read for all those who think spiritual reading is complex, and for all others too'—Sonal Kalra, national editor, entertainment and lifestyle, *Hindustan Times*

'It's a blessing to be at the feet of the Master and seek his guidance for life! This book is another such gift to read and imbibe. It has incredible offerings for life and living with healthy zest. It zapped me straightaway and I was on till I finished. The way Sadhguru puts it, it is lucid, simple, and extraordinarily matter-of-fact'—Satya Paul, fashion designer

'*Three Truths* has become my bible, it's like a vitamin for one's well-being. When I read something here that clicks with me, I instantly feel the urge to share that thought with others. Thank you for making it so simple and accessible'—Namita Devidayal, author and journalist

'For many of us who are busy chasing life—which seems to run faster than us—this book give us some, dare I say, "easy" things that all of us, regardless of where we stand in life, can adopt to enhance our living experience by just a bit. It breaks our notion of well-being and helps focus on what is truly important for our well-being'—Nandini Wamorkar, CEO, Ajna Advisors Pvt. Ltd

'As a sceptic of self-help books, I accepted the book with my usual high dose of suspicion. Yet, page by page, my suspicion took a seat in the background as the book revealed itself as a clear, well-organized, practical and enjoyable read. More than anything, I was impressed by its tantalizing effect which created a longing to know more, to dwell deeper on the issues that Sadhguru brought to the fore'—Cristina Ioana Dragomir, PhD, assistant professor, State University of New York

'An outstanding self-help book by a world-renowned yogi and mystic; it stands out amid the surfeit of advisory self-transformational books. One that provokes us to try out effective techniques which will hasten our evolutionary journey in the elusive quest for the mundane and the mysterious. Even a sceptic, who diligently practises these techniques, could experience the joy of having found the Holy Grail at last'—Rahul B. Patil, finance consultant

'This isn't a self-help book. It's a book of awakening. Pragmatic and filled with so much logic, I almost felt silly for not having realized these things earlier. Yet the grace that exudes from his words provides comfort and I know that in uncovering these truths, I am not alone'—Jean Esther, writer, lecturer, nurse

'Sadhguru's ability to articulate, convey and explain an abstract concept to a diverse audience is amazing. In this book, Sadhguru, with the help of his dedicated and devoted team, is able to put the most important information people ought to know about well-being. It is a must-read'—Inna Jones, artist

'A book which delivers life-changing wisdom in bite-size pieces for each of us to experience, absorb and implement in our daily lives. The narrative in every chapter resonates with our perpetual dilemmas at both the mundane and esoteric levels. After reading the book, it feels like the answers are finally coming'—Prasanthi Guda, career counsellor

'Every word from the mystic makes you realize how little you know of how to live. This is the perfect guide to take you from merely living to being alive'—Rajesh Saathi, screenwriter and ad film director, Keroscene Films

'A power-packed magic potion in the form of a book! It has reiterated my belief in my motto of life—"love life and it will love you back". Simple yet powerful concepts that make living itself such a joyful experience. Sadhguru's profundity through his simple writing never ceases to amaze and overwhelm my husband, Desh, and me. As for me, I keep my magic potion handy, always'—Archana Chaurasia Kapoor, MD and CEO, Drishtique

THREE TRUTHS OF
WELL BEING

SADHGURU

EMPOWER YOUR BODY, MIND
AND ENERGY FOR JOYFUL LIVING

PENGUIN BOOKS

PENGUIN ANANDA

Published by the Penguin Group

Penguin Books India Pvt. Ltd, 7th Floor, Infinity Tower C, DLF Cyber City,
Gurgaon 122 002, Haryana, India

Penguin Group (USA) Inc., 375 Hudson Street, New York, New York 10014, USA

Penguin Group (Canada), 90 Eglinton Avenue East, Suite 700, Toronto,
Ontario, M4P 2Y3, Canada

Penguin Books Ltd, 80 Strand, London WC2R 0RL, England

Penguin Ireland, 25 St Stephen's Green, Dublin 2, Ireland (a division of
Penguin Books Ltd)

Penguin Group (Australia), 707 Collins Street, Melbourne, Victoria 3008, Australia

Penguin Group (NZ), 67 Apollo Drive, Rosedale, Auckland 0632, New Zealand

Penguin Books (South Africa) (Pty) Ltd, Block D, Rosebank Office Park,
181 Jan Smuts Avenue, Parktown North, Johannesburg 2193, South Africa

Penguin Books Ltd, Registered Offices: 80 Strand, London WC2R 0RL, England

First published in Penguin Ananda by Penguin Books India 2013
This paperback edition published 2014

ISBN 9780143421276

For sale in the Indian Subcontinent only

Typeset in Minion by R. Ajith Kumar
Printed at Replika Press Pvt. Ltd, India

A PENGUIN RANDOM HOUSE COMPANY

Contents

MIND

ENERGY

Contents

Introduction

Sadhguru and a *self-help* book?

It seems like an odd – even outrageous – proposition. Those familiar with his style know that Sadhguru doesn't give answers as much as provoke questions. He once described himself as 'a rough and tumble' guru. And one can see why. There's nothing chicken-soupy about Sadhguru. His approach is straight-talking, energetic, unsentimental. Far from avuncular. 'If you are thirsty and you ask me for water, I will put salt in your mouth because if you become thirsty enough you will find the source of water,' he often says.

How then did this book happen?

Surprisingly, because Sadhguru agreed. 'I don't like saying no,' he said simply when the idea was first mooted. He only laid down one precondition: don't dumb it down.

For those at the Isha Yoga Centre who worked on this book (chiefly Maa Idaa, aided by Bhairagini Maa Martha, Tina and Nathalie, with inputs from me), the challenge was considerable. For one, with his hectic schedule, Sadhguru doesn't have the time to write. This meant working largely with transcripts of his discourses, interspersed with conversations with him whenever possible. Transposing the spoken word on to the printed page wasn't easy. We decided to preserve the spoken flavour as far as possible. This may account for moments of awkward syntax and non-linearity. But the idea was to let readers feel his distinctive presence through the text. And the fluid patterns of a conversational mode seemed preferable to a more stilted correctness.

The other challenge was how to simplify without trivializing; how to be accessible without turning anaemic; how to reach a first-time reader without alienating those who know Sadhguru as a spiritual master and sage.

Sadhguru's wisdom encompasses the material and the mystical. How much of what to include was another question. It would be dishonest to present Sadhguru as either a New Age Life Coach or as a religious preacher. He is neither. He is a yogi. This means he is capable of sounding both logical and non-rational, uber-cool and ancient at the same time. He can be more irreverent than a diehard atheist. He can also be way more esoteric than your common or garden psychic.

But amputating the text to fit a reader's comfort zone didn't seem like the answer. The Isha Publications team streamlined and pruned, keeping in mind the demands of the self-help genre. But the idea was also to retain some of the zigzag and freshness of a conversation with a mystic. The result is a book that's nifty and worldly and practical. Well being is the aim. But because it is Sadhguru, the book is also infused with an ancient yogic wisdom that compels us to reappraise fundamental ideas about being human and being alive. Hence the more esoteric moments with which this text is liberally peppered, particularly in the last section.

Perhaps the best way to describe Sadhguru is as an alchemist. That's a key to reading this book. Don't be fooled by its simplicity. On the other hand, don't be daunted if some of the advice is challenging to implement. Somewhere along the way, you're likely to get the scent of something more than a heap of concepts, tips, anecdotes and jokes. That is the scent of a master. Someone capable not just of teaching, but of transforming. It is the scent that drew me to him many years ago. The scent of something real.

Yes, this is a self-help manual. Pragmatic. Do-it-yourself. Down-to-earth. There is an Isha Kriya DVD at the close of it which is the most vital tool of self-empowerment that the book offers. You could try putting it into practice as often as you can. Its author says you can become the author of your own well being and that isn't an idle promise. The practice does bring clarity, aliveness, joy.

But since this is a book by a spiritual master, it is also a manual with a dash of grace. Allow the book and the DVD to happen to you. And on those days when the self-help is hard going and the instructions feel like so many words on the page, allow the alchemy to take over. It works.

Arundhathi Subramaniam

Prologue

Joy for most people is a rare visitor in their lives. The intention of this book is to make joy your constant companion.

Joy is not a goal by itself. But it is a background milieu that is needed for any aspect of your life to happen wonderfully. Whether you eat, dance, sing, love, live or die, if it isn't there as a backdrop, you will have to drag your way through life. But once joy is your constant companion, life just breezes through you.

Sadhguru

'Four Idiots': The Yogic Way

**'The word "yoga" means, in your experience, everything
has become one. Yoga means union.'**

It happened once. Four men were walking in the forest. The
first was a *gnana yogi*, the second was a *bhakti yogi*, the third
was a *karma yogi*, and the fourth was a *kriya yogi*.

Usually, these four people can never be together. The gnana
yogi has total disdain for every other type of yoga. His is the
yoga of intelligence, and normally, an intellectual has complete
disdain for everybody else, particularly these bhakti types, who
look upward and chant God's name all the time. They look like
a bunch of idiots to him.

But a bhakti yogi, a devotee, thinks all this gnana, karma and
kriya yoga is a waste of time. He pities the others who don't see
that when God is here, all you need to do is hold His hand and
walk. All this mind-splitting philosophy, this bone-bending

yoga, is not needed; God is here, because God is everywhere.

Then there is the karma yogi, the man of action. He thinks all the other types of yogis, with their fancy philosophies, are just lazy.

But a kriya yogi is the most disdainful of all. He laughs at everyone. Don't they know that all of existence is energy? If you don't transform your energy, whether you long for God or you long for anything else, nothing is going to happen. There will be no transformation.

These four people customarily can't get along. But today they happened to be walking together in the forest and a storm broke out. It grew very intense and began raining heavily. They started running, looking for shelter.

The bhakti yogi, the devotion man, said, 'In this direction there is an ancient temple. Let's go there.' (He's a devotee; he knows the geography of temples very well!)

They all ran in that direction. They came to an ancient temple; all the walls had crumbled long ago; just the roof and four columns remained. They rushed into the temple; not out of love for God, but just to escape the rain.

There was a deity in the centre. They ran towards it. The rain was lashing down from every direction. There was no other place to go, so they moved closer and closer. Finally, there was no alternative. They just hugged the deity and sat down.

The moment these four people hugged the idol, there was a huge fifth presence. Suddenly, God appeared.

In all their four minds the same question arose: Why now? They wondered, 'We expounded so many philosophies, did so many pujas, served so many people, did so much body-breaking *sadhana* (spiritual practice), but you didn't come. Now when we're just escaping the rain, you turn up. Why?'

God said, 'At last you four idiots got together!'

~

If these dimensions – body, mind (which includes both your thoughts and emotions) and energy – don't walk together, human beings will be one big mess. Right now, for most people, these three dimensions are aligned in different directions. Your mind is thinking and feeling one way; your physical body is going another way; your energy another way.

Yoga is simply the science of aligning these three dimensions.

When we say 'yoga', for many of you it probably means some impossible physical postures. That is not what we are referring to here. That is 'Columbus yoga' – a rebound from the West. Yoga simply means to be in perfect tune. When you are in yoga, your body, mind and energy and existence are in absolute harmony.

When your body and mind are in a relaxed state and at a certain level of blissfulness, you can be free of so many nagging ailments. Let us say, you go and sit in your office with a nagging headache. Your headache is not a major disease, but just that throbbing could take away some of your enthusiasm for work and perhaps some of your capability for that day. But with the practice of yoga, your body and mind can be kept at the highest possible peak.

Yoga is simply the technology of creating inner situations the way you want them. When you fine-tune yourself to such a point where everything functions beautifully within you, naturally, the best of your abilities will simply flow out of you. When you are happy, your energies always function better. Have you noticed that when you are joyful you have endless energy? Even if you don't eat, if you don't sleep, you can go on and on. A little happiness is liberating you from your normal limitations of energy and capability. Conversely, when you activate your energies, you can function in a different way altogether.

Yoga is the science of activating your inner energies in such a way that your body and mind function at their highest potential. You may believe many things about yourself, about who you are, but fundamentally you are just a certain amount of life energy. Modern science says that the whole existence is just energy manifesting itself in different ways. If this is so, then you are also just a little bit of energy functioning in a particular way. Science is telling you that this same energy which you call 'myself' can sit here as a rock, lie there as mud, stand up as a tree, bark as a dog, or sit here as you.

The cosmos is one big organism. Your life is not independent of the universe. You cannot live without the world around you because every moment there is a transaction, a very deep relationship between the two. What you exhale, the trees around you inhale; what they exhale, you inhale. The problem is just that we have subjugated our intelligence to our individuality. This loss of organic existence is the reason why human beings are experiencing such high levels of conflict, distress and disease in their lives.

Although everything in the universe is the same energy, it functions at different levels of capability, in different forms.

Similarly, while all human beings are made of the same energy, we still do not function at the same level of capability. Capability or creative talent – your ability to do things in the world and to experience life – is just a certain way your energy functions. This energy functions in one plant to create rose flowers; in another plant it functions to create jasmine. If you gain a little bit of mastery over your own energies, you will see that things that you never imagined possible, you will be able to do, simply and naturally.

With the same material that we build huge buildings today, initially people were building little huts. We thought we could only dig mud and make pots or bricks out of it. Now we dig the earth and make computers, cars, and even spacecrafts out of it. It is the same material; we have just started using it for higher and higher possibilities. Our inner energies are similar. There is a whole technology of how to use this energy for higher possibilities. Every human being must explore and know this. Otherwise, our lives become very limited and accidental.

Once you start activating your inner energies, your capabilities emerge in a different sphere altogether. Yoga is a tool to find this ultimate expression to life.

So, yoga does not mean twisting your body, tying your limbs into knots or holding your breath or performing some other circus. The word 'yoga' means, in your experience, everything has become one. Yoga means union.

What is this union? What can unite with what?

Right now, there is something called 'me' and there is something called the 'other'. This 'me' and the 'other' can get extended to groups of people, communities and nations, but fundamentally, 'me' and the 'other' is the basis of conflict in the universe.

What is 'me', and what is not 'me'? In your experience, right now, what are the things which you call 'myself'?

What you call 'myself' are your body, your mind (which includes your thought and your emotion) and your energies. Your energies may not be in your experience, but you can easily infer that if your body and mind function as they do, there must be some kind of energy empowering them. These three realities are what you can work with: body, mind and energy.

The whole point of yoga, or the spiritual process, is to bring you to an experience that if you sit here, there is no such thing as 'you' and 'me'. It is all me – or all you. Anything that leads to this union, whichever way you get there, is called yoga.

How many ways are there to reach this ultimate union? You can only work with what you have. If you talk about something that you do not know, you have a choice: either to believe it or disbelieve it. Suppose I start talking about a particular god, you either have to believe my god or disbelieve my god. Either way, this will only take you into fanciful imagination, not growth. Realizing where you are right now existentially and then taking the next step is growth. The whole process of yoga is to take you from something that you know to the next step, into the unknown.

If you employ your body and try to reach your ultimate nature, we call this *karma yoga*, yoga of action. If you employ your intelligence and try to reach your ultimate nature, we call this *gnana yoga*, yoga of intelligence. If you employ your emotion and try to reach your ultimate nature, we call this *bhakti yoga*, yoga of devotion or emotion. If you transform your energies and try to reach your ultimate nature, we call this *kriya yoga*, yoga of transforming energies.

All these aspects have to function together; only then you get somewhere. Everyone is a unique combination of these, because these ingredients come together in different ways in every person.

So, to know well being all you need is just a little mastery over these dimensions: your body, your mind and your energy. Being successful in the world just depends on your ability to harness these three dimensions in an appropriate manner, according to the situations in which you exist and the activity that you want to do.

The problem is that religious nuts around the world have exported everything that is beautiful about a human being to the other world. If you talk of love, they speak of divine love. If you talk of bliss, they speak of divine bliss; peace, divine peace. We have forgotten that these are all *human* qualities. A human being is fully capable of joy, of love, of peace. Why do you want to export these to heaven?

There is so much talk of God and heaven mainly because human beings have not realized the immensity of being human. To be joyful and peaceful within yourself every moment of your life, to be able to perceive life beyond its physical limitations – these are not superhuman qualities. These are human possibilities.

This yoga is not about being superhuman; this is about realizing that being human is super.

BODY

The Only Gift

'A human being is equipped to live his life in a most miraculous way – if only he is in touch with that source of creation within himself.'

The most intimate part of physical creation for an individual is his own body. This is the first gift he is aware of.

But the body is not just the first gift; it is the only one. In the yogic sciences, there is no such thing as mind or soul. Everything – from the gross to the subtle – is just the body manifesting itself in different dimensions. There are five sheaths or dimensions of body, which we will talk about later in this book.

For now let us look at the physical body. It is designed and structured to function by itself without much of your participation. You don't have to make the heart beat, make the liver perform all its complex chemistry, or even have to try to breathe; everything that is needed for your physical existence is

> But the body is not just the first gift; it is the only one.

happening on its own.

The physical body is a self-contained, quite complete instrument. If you are fascinated by gadgets, there isn't a better one. Every little thing you explore in this body is quite incredible, isn't it? This is the most sophisticated piece of machinery on the planet. It is the highest level of mechanics that you can imagine, the highest level of electronics that you can think of, the highest level of electrical connectivity that you can dream of, the highest level of computing capability that you could conceive of.

Let us say you eat a banana in the afternoon. By evening, this banana has become you. Charles Darwin told you that to make a monkey into a human being it took millions of years, but in a few hours you are capable of making even a banana into a human being! Not a small feat. This means the very source of creation is functioning from within you.

There is a certain level of intelligence and competence that exists within you, which is beyond your logical mind, which can transform a banana into an object of technological excellence. This is what yoga is about – finding access to that dimension, that intelligence, that capability which can transform a banana into a human being within a few hours.

If you could achieve that transformation consciously, instead of unconsciously, if you could bring even a drop of that intelligence into your daily life, you would live magically, not miserably.

Eternal Question

'The very basis of a spiritual process is to explore the possibilities of the body and to go beyond its limitations.'

It takes a certain amount of intelligence and awareness for a person to see the limitations of this fantastic gadget. Gadgetry is fine, but it still does not take you anywhere. It just springs out of the earth and gets you back to the earth.

Isn't it enough?

If you look at it from the perspective of the body, it *is* quite enough. But a dimension beyond the physical has somehow got trapped in the physical. This dimension, without which there is no life, has somehow infused itself into the physical.

Life is one thing, but the source of life is another. In every creature, in every plant, in every seed, the source of life is functioning. But the source of life in a human being has more prominence. It is because of this prominence that all the simple or even wonderful things that the physical offers seem irrelevant beyond a point, to many people.

Because of this one aspect, human beings seem to be in a constant struggle between the physical and that which is beyond the physical. Though you have the compulsiveness of the physical, you also have the consciousness of not being just physical. There are two basic forces within you. Most people see them as in conflict. One is the instinct of self-preservation, which compels you to build walls around yourself to protect yourself. But another part of you is longing to constantly expand, trying to become boundless.

The walls of self-preservation that you build for today are the walls of self-imprisonment for tomorrow. Many limitations that you establish in your life as a protection for yourself today, feel like constraints tomorrow, and you want to break them only to build a bigger prison for yourself. But day after tomorrow, the bigger prison also feels like a restriction, and you want to break it and move to the next stage.

These two longings – to preserve and to expand – are not opposing forces. They are related to two different aspects of who you are. One belongs to the physical; another belongs to the dimension beyond the physical. One force helps you root yourself well on this planet; another takes you beyond. Self-preservation needs to be limited to the physical body. If one has the necessary awareness to separate the two, there is no conflict. But if you limit yourself to the physical, then instead of working in collaboration, these two fundamental forces become a source of conflict. All the struggle of humanity in terms of 'should I be spiritual or materialistic?' springs from this ignorance.

> The walls of self-preservation that you build for today are the walls of self-imprisonment for tomorrow.

When you say 'spirituality', you are talking about a dimension which is beyond the physical. The fundamentals of spiritual longing are to transcend the limitations of the physical. But because your instinct of self-preservation keeps telling you, 'Unless you have a wall you are not safe,' unconsciously you go on building walls all the time. It is not the Creator's unwillingness to open up a different possibility that you are struggling with. What you are struggling with are just the concrete walls that you have built around yourself.

That is why the yogic system does not talk about God. It does not talk about the Ultimate Being. It does not talk about the Creator. If we talk about the Ultimate, you will become hallucinatory. We are only talking about what is blocking you because that is what needs to be attended to. Bondage is one hundred per cent of your making. The ropes that bind you or the walls that block you – this is all you need to look at. You have no work with existence. You have work only with the existence that you have created.

If we have to use an analogy, we could see gravity and Grace, for example, as opposites. Gravity is one aspect of life which, in a way, is related to the fundamental instinct of self-preservation in a human being. We are rooted to the planet right now because of gravity. We have a body today only because of gravity. Gravity is trying to hold you down; Grace is something that is trying to lift you up. If you are released from the physical forces of existence, then Grace bursts forth in your life.

As gravity is active, so is Grace constantly active. It is just that you have to make yourself available to it. With gravity you have no choice; anyway you are available to it. But with Grace, you have to make yourself receptive. Whatever kind of *sadhana* you may do, ultimately, you are just working towards making yourself available to Grace. If you are strongly identified with the physical, gravity is all that you will know.

> Existence has not blocked anything for you. If you are willing you can access the whole universe.

Access to something beyond the physical is also access to Grace. So, if your experience of life transcends the limitations of the physical, you are available to Grace. Suddenly you seem to function like magic. It is just like if you were the only one to ride a bicycle you would also look magical. Other people may think you *are* magic, but you know you are just beginning to become receptive to a different dimension of life. This possibility is wide open for everybody.

Life has left everything open for you. Existence has not blocked anything for anyone. If you are willing, you can access the whole universe. Somebody said, 'Knock, and it shall open.' You don't even have to knock because there is no door; it is wide open. You just have to walk through, that's all.

THE NEXT STEP

You may have noticed this about yourself: when you are feeling pleasant, you want to expand; when you are fearful, you want to contract. Try this. Sit in front of a plant or tree. Remind yourself that you are inhaling what the tree is exhaling, and exhaling what the tree is inhaling. Even if it is not yet experiential for you, establish a psychological connection with the plant. Repeat this five times a day. After a few days, you will start connecting with everything around you differently. You won't limit yourself to a tree. (Using this simple process, we at Isha have unleashed an environmental initiative in the state of Tamil Nadu, under which eighteen million trees have been planted since 2004. We spent several years planting trees in people's minds, which is the most difficult terrain! Now transplanting those on to land happens so much more effortlessly.)

Physical and Metaphysical

'However spiritual you are, you still have to carry the body with you.'

I am often asked why spirituality seems other-worldly and life-denying. Why, people ask, must we choose to become either spiritual or materialistic? Why can't we enjoy both?

Actually there are no two such categories. Your body, mind and energy are one, isn't it? Only if you get shot can these be separated! Or if you grow in your awareness they can be separated; that is different.

But is somebody hundred per cent materialistic? Is somebody hundred per cent spiritual? There is no such thing. However spiritual you are you have to carry your body with you, you have to feed it, wash it and clothe it. So, you are still materialistic. Can you give up your being and just live with your body? No. So, you are still spiritual.

The difference is just this: some beg for everything in their life while others earn it for themselves. Some people have to beg for their happiness, love and peace and most essential things in their life from somebody else. Only their food they earn; for everything else they beg. Another kind of person earns his love, his peace and his joy by himself; he only begs for his food. If he wants to earn his food, that is no big deal, but right now he thinks it is not so important, and he begs for it. That is the only difference between the renunciate and the worldly person.

After all, what is most of humanity doing? Just eating, sleeping, reproducing and dying. You may believe you are doing many things, but when the moment of death comes to you and you turn back and look at your life, you'll find that all you have done is complicate the survival process. Just the simple process of life – which every worm, insect, dog, cat and bird can handle – human beings have become incapable of going through. At the end of their lives they are so hurt by everything around them. Unfortunately, with age most people are not becoming wise; they are becoming wounded.

I am not saying you should not enjoy the physical things around you. Sex in the body is fine. Money in the wallet is fine. It is only a problem when they enter your mind.

Beyond Survival

'Whatever you experience beyond the five sense perceptions is not in terms of physical reality; it is in a different dimension. That dimension, if you want to call it God, you can call it God; if you want to call it power, you can call it power. Or if you just want to call it "myself", you can call it "myself".'

Right now, whatever you have known, either of the world or yourself, has come to you only through your five sense organs – by seeing, hearing, smelling, tasting and touching. If these five senses go to sleep, you neither know the world nor yourself.

The sense organs are limited; the very way they are made, the five senses can perceive only that which is physical. If your perception is limited to the five senses, naturally the play and scope of your life will be only physical. The senses perceive everything only in comparison with something else.

If I touch a steel rod and it feels cool, it is simply because my body temperature is in a certain way. Suppose I lower my temperature and touch it, now it will feel warm to me.

Sense perception is giving you a distorted impression of reality because sense organs experience everything only in comparison with something else. Whatever experience you have through the five sense perceptions is sufficient only for survival. But if you are seeking something beyond survival, then the sense perceptions are not enough.

All yogic practices are fundamentally aimed at giving you an experience beyond the five senses. Whatever you experience beyond the five sense perceptions is not in terms of physical reality; it is in a different dimension. If you want to call that dimension God, you can call it God; if you want to call it power, you can call it power. Or if you just want to call it 'myself', you can call it 'myself'.

If you are really interested in knowing life in its depth, you must see how to enhance your perception. This moment, if you fall asleep, suddenly people around you will disappear, the world will disappear, and even *you* will disappear. You are still alive, everybody around is alive and is in existence, but in your experience everything evaporates, because these five sense organs have shut down.

Anything that you experience has happened only within you. But the human predicament is just this: the very seat of your experience is within you, but your perception is all outward bound. You can see what is outside, but you cannot see what is inside. There is so much activity in the body, but you cannot hear it. There is so much blood flowing inside you, and you cannot feel it, but if an ant crawls upon your hand you can sense it. All the sense organs are outward bound, but all the experience is within you. This is why there is such a big disconnect.

The sense organs got turned on at the moment of your birth because they are necessary for your survival. But if you want to turn inward, you have no perception yet, because it takes a little bit of striving. It does not matter whether

> All yogic practices are fundamentally aimed at giving you an experience beyond the five senses.

you want to know the process of creation or you just want to live peacefully – what you need to do is enhance your perception to at least some level where your body, mind and energy happen the way you want them.

Whether we are doctors, policemen, engineers, or whatever else, fundamentally, it is our perception of what is in front of us this moment that decides how effective we can be and how much we can do on here. This perception can be raised to various levels through certain inner mechanisms.

Let us start from the mundane: if your sense perception expands beyond its present boundaries, when food appears in front of you, you will simply know how this food would behave in your system. But most human beings have not accessed such capabilities within themselves. So, from something as simple as this to the ultimate possibility, the inner perception brings a completely new dimension into one's life.

The common questions are: Is it very difficult to rise above my senses? Do I have to withdraw to a Himalayan cave to do this?

The answer is not at all. Any human being who is willing to dedicate just a few minutes of his life per day can begin to know this. This possibility is not sitting somewhere in the mountains; it is within you. What is within you is not inaccessible to you; it is just that you are either busy or preoccupied with what is happening outside. What is happening in your mind is also a reflection of the outside, so in other words, you have never paid any attention to the inward. It is just a lack of attention which has denied people this possibility.

If people develop the simple habit of paying a little bit of attention to themselves, it would definitely change the essence of their lives in so many ways. Just spending fifteen to twenty minutes a day on this process is all it takes. The experience of transcending your limitations comes from within you. Transcendence can only happen if you are truly willing; otherwise no power on earth can move you.

THE NEXT STEP

Start by paying attention to everything you think is yourself: your clothes, your makeup, your hair, your skin, your thoughts, your emotions. Know that none of this is you. Keep discounting all that is not you. There is no need to make any conclusion about what truth is. Truth is not a conclusion. If you keep the false conclusions that you make at bay, truth will definitely dawn. It's like your experience of the night: the sun has not gone; it's just that the planet is looking the other way. You're thinking, reading, talking about the self, because you're too busy looking the other way. You haven't paid enough attention to know what the self really is. What is needed is not a conclusion but a turnaround.

Listening to Life

'The science of using the body to hasten your evolutionary process is hatha yoga.'

When you experience everything as oneness in your consciousness, then you are in yoga. To attain that unity within you, there are many ways. You work with the body, then you move to the breath, then to the mind, then to the inner self. Like this, many steps have been created, but they are only different facets of yoga. It is important that all of them are addressed in a very balanced way, all at once, as a single unit. There is really no division; yoga employs all aspects of who you are.

The body is a very large part of who you are right now. The science of using the body to hasten your evolutionary process is hatha yoga.

The body itself has its own attitudes, its own ego, its own nature. Let us say you decide, 'Starting tomorrow, I will get up at five in the morning and go for a walk.' You set the alarm. The alarm rings. You want to get up, but your body says, 'Shut up and sleep.' It has its own way, doesn't it? Hatha yoga is a way of working with the body, a way of disciplining, purifying and preparing the body for higher levels of energy and possibilities.

Hatha yoga is *not* exercise. Understanding the mechanics of the body, creating a certain atmosphere, and then using body postures to drive your energy in specific directions is what hatha yoga or *yogasana*s are about.

'*Asana*' means a 'posture'. That kind of posture which allows you to reach your higher nature is a yogasana. There are other dimensions to this, but to put it in the simplest way, just by observing the way someone is sitting, you can almost know what is happening with him, if you have known him long enough. If you have observed yourself, when you are angry, you sit one way; if you are happy, you sit another way; if you are depressed, you sit another way. For every different level of consciousness or mental and emotional situation that you go through, your body naturally tends to assume certain postures. The converse of this is the science of asanas. If you consciously get your body into different postures, you can elevate your consciousness.

The body can become a means for your spiritual

> For every different level of consciousness or mental and emotional situation that you go through, your body naturally tends to assume certain postures.

> The body can become a means for your spiritual growth or it can become a major barrier.

growth or it can become a major barrier. Suppose some part of your body – your hand, leg or back, for instance – is hurting. When it is hurting badly it is hard to aspire to anything higher because that becomes the biggest thing. Right now if you have a backache, the biggest thing in the universe is your backache. Other people may not understand that, but for the person who is going through it, that *is* the biggest thing. Even if God appears you will ask for your backache to go! You will not ask for anything else because the physical body has such power over you. If it is not functioning well, it can take away all other aspirations from your life. Whatever you may fancy, all your longings just disappear once the body starts hurting – because to look beyond that takes an enormous amount of strength, which most people do not possess.

There are thousands of people who have overcome spinal problems by doing simple asanas. They had been told by doctors that they would definitely have to undergo surgery, but never had to. Your back can be restored to such an excellent condition that you will never need to go to a chiropractor. It is not only your spine that becomes flexible; *you* become flexible. Once you are flexible, you are willing to listen, not just to someone's talk; you are willing to listen to life. Learning to listen is the essence of a sensible life.

Dedicating a certain amount of effort and time to see that

the body does not become a barrier is important. A painful body can become a major obstacle, and so can a compulsive body.

Simple compulsions, whether they are about the body wanting to relieve itself, or of lust, can rule you so strongly that they will not allow you to look beyond; the physical body becomes a major entity. But the body is only a part of you; it should not become the whole of you. Asanas level the body down to its natural place.

Another aspect of hatha yoga, when one wants to move into deeper dimensions of meditation, is that it allows for a higher possibility of energy. If you want your energies to surge upwards, it is very important that the body's pipeline should be conducive to this. If it is blocked, it will not work; or else, something will burst. Preparing the body sufficiently before one goes into more intense forms of meditation is very important. Hatha yoga ensures that the body takes it gently and joyfully.

For a lot of people, spiritual growth happens very painfully because the necessary preparation does not take place. Most human beings have unfortunately let themselves lapse into a condition where the external situations mould them and direct them entirely. Whether it is the wisdom of the world or spiritual possibilities, they get the point only when they are knocked around by life. Even then, only some become wise; others become wounded. It is this possibility of transforming a potential wound into a source of wisdom that leads one to a state of freedom. If one has put in the necessary preparation, it can be a wonderful experience of growth. It is becoming a norm that growth must be painful. It can be done blissfully but because both the body and mind have not been prepared, all change happens painfully. Asanas prepare you for growth and transformation by equipping you with a solid foundation.

Today, the hatha yoga that people are learning is not in its classical form, not in its full depth and dimension. Largely the 'studio yoga' that you see today is unfortunately just the physical aspect of it. Just teaching the physical aspect of yoga is like having a stillborn baby. That is not only no good, it is a tragedy. If you want a live process, it needs to be taught in a certain way.

Hatha yoga does not mean twisting your body, standing on your head, or holding your breath. There was a time when I was personally teaching hatha yoga as a two-day programme. People would burst with joy; tears of ecstasy would flow, simply doing asanas. That is the way yoga needs to be done. Unfortunately, the hatha yoga in the world today brings peace for some, is healthful for others, and is a painful circus for many.

Most yogis just use the simple postures to overcome their limitations. That is all I learned when I was eleven years of age – just a few simple postures. It is just the *way* it is done that makes the difference.

THE NEXT STEP

Within your own home, office, and among your friends, do you see everyone has different levels of perception? Just observe this closely. If you know a few people who seem to have a greater clarity of perception than others, watch how they conduct their body. You will understand what I mean by the geometry of your existence. Just the way you hold your body determines almost everything about you.

One way of listening to life is paying attention to life experientially, not intellectually or emotionally. Choose any one thing about yourself: your breath, your heartbeat, your pulse, your little finger. Just stay with it for eleven minutes at a time. Keep doing this as often as you can. You will find your experience of life changing dramatically.

Effort to Effortlessness

'When you reach the peak of effort, you become effortless.'

Logically, somebody who never put effort into anything should be the master of effortlessness – but it is not so. If you want to know effortlessness, you need to know effort. When you reach the peak of effort, you become effortless. Only a man who has been working knows rest. A man who is always resting knows no rest; he only sinks into laziness, lethargy. This is the way of life.

For the Russian ballet dancer Nijinsky, his whole life was dance. There were moments when he would leap to heights that seemed humanly impossible by any scientific principle. Even if one's muscles are at peak performance, there is still a limit to how high one can jump. But in some moments he would go beyond that limit.

People asked him, 'How do you manage this?'

He said, 'There is no way I can ever do it. When Nijinsky is not there, only then it happens.'

When man is constantly giving a hundred per cent of

himself, a point comes when he goes beyond that limit into total effortlessness. By simply sitting around, effortlessness will not happen. There are some people nowadays, who say they will go for Zen because it means doing nothing. Actually, Zen involves that kind of tremendous activity that very few people can perform. In performing this activity, you reach a state of non-doing, where you are not the doer any more. It is in such states that one knows transcendence or a taste of the beyond. If one achieves such states through intense activity as Nijinsky and many others have, those moments will always be cherished as magical moments. But if one arrives at the same state through the intensity of inactivity, then it is a yogic posture which allows an enduring state of transcendence.

The very essence of *dhyana,* or meditativeness, is that you push yourself to the highest possible intensity where, after some time, there is no effort. You can simply be. It is in these absolutely non-compulsive states of mind and existence that the necessary atmosphere is set for the flowering of inner genius. As societies and individuals allow every moment to pass without creating the atmosphere for such a flowering, a possibility of humanity has gone waste. There is much infantile talk about heaven and its pleasures only because the immensity of being human has not been explored. If your humanity overflows, divinity will follow and serve you. It has no other choice.

Cosmic Download

'The body is like an antenna – if you hold it in the right position it can just grasp everything in existence.'

This whole existence is a certain kind of geometry, and so is your body. This makes it a tremendous possibility.

Probably these days, this is no longer a problem, but just a few years ago, after every storm, you had to go up and adjust your TV antenna. Only if it was angled in a certain way did you have television reception. Or else, as you were watching your soap opera or a cricket match, suddenly a blizzard would appear on your screen. You had to fine-tune the antenna.

This body is like that: if you hold it in the right position, it can receive the whole cosmos. If you hold it in some other way, you will know nothing beyond the five senses.

Your body is like a barometer. If you know how to watch it, it can tell you everything about you and the world around you. The body never lies to you, so in yoga, we learn to trust the body. We transform the very physical body from a series of compulsive processes to a conscious process, and convert it into a powerful instrument of perception and knowing.

There is a whole science and technology of how to make this body more than just a heap of food, an accumulation of what we have taken from the earth, and more than the compulsions of our chemistry, flesh and blood. If you know how to read the body, it tells you all your potential, your limitations – your past, present and future. That is why the fundamental yoga starts with the body.

> Your body is like a barometer. If you know how to watch it, it tells you everything about you and the world that you live in.

It is as simple as this. The more you know about your phone or any other gadget, the better you can use it. A few years ago, the cell phone companies in India did a survey, and they found out that ninety-seven per cent of the people are using only seven per cent of the capabilities that are there in a phone. (I'm not talking about the smart phone here, but the 'dumb' one!)

Even in that little gadget, you are using only seven per cent. Now, this body of yours is *the* gadget. Every other gadget on the planet has come out of this. What percentage of *this* gadget do you think you are employing?

Well below one per cent. To conduct your life in the material world, your survival process, you do not even need one per cent of what this body is. We are doing all kinds of trivial things with it because right now our whole perception of life is limited to the physical nature of existence. But your body is capable of perceiving the whole cosmos. If you prepare it properly, it can grasp everything in this existence, because all that happens to this existence in some way is happening to this physical body.

The Next Step

A human being breathes twelve to fifteen times per minute, normally. If you reduce it to eleven, you will know the ways of the outermost part of the earth or the atmosphere (i.e. you will become meteorologically sensitive). If you reduce it to nine, you will know the language of the other creatures on this planet. If you reduce it to seven, you will know the very language of the earth. If you reduce it to five, you will know the language of the source of creation. This is not about increasing your aerobic capacity. Nor is it about forcefully depriving yourself of breath. A combination of hatha yoga and kriya will gradually increase your lung capacity, but above all, will help you achieve a certain alignment, a certain ease, so that your system evolves to a state of stability where there is no static, no crackle; it just perceives everything.

Body Planet

**'Whatever happens to this planet happens to you, because
in your physical body, you are nothing more than the
planet.'**

Your body is just the food that you eat; the food that you eat
is just the earth. You are just a small outcrop of this earth
prancing around. Whatever happens to the planet happens to
you too – in some very subtle way.

This planet is part of a larger body which we call the solar
system. Whatever happens to that system happens to the planet.
This solar system is part of a larger body we call the universe or
the cosmos. Maybe it is beyond your mental perception right
now, but everything that is happening to any part of the cosmos
is also in some way happening to this planet. And whatever
happens to this planet happens to you, because in your physical
body, you are nothing more than the planet.

If you keep your body in a certain way, you would be aware of every small and subtle change taking place on earth. In a remote way, you can also be aware of what is happening in the cosmos. Once you become sensitive to it, your whole body feels everything happening around you. If you spend more time and pay attention to the earth and the ways of the earth, this sensitivity will increase dramatically.

I was living on a farm for a few years. There was a man in the local village who had a hearing impairment. Because he could barely hear, he could not respond to people, so they thought

> Whatever happens to the planet happens to you too – in some very subtle way.

he was an idiot, and the village rejected him and made fun of him. I employed him as my man on the farm. He was a nice companion to have because I don't like to talk, and he could not talk because he could not hear. So, no problem!

Those were the days before tractors; it was all bullocks and ploughing. One day, suddenly, at four o'clock in the morning, I saw him preparing the plough.

I asked him, 'What's happening?'

He said, 'I am getting ready to plough.'

I said, 'What are you going to plough? There is no rain.'

He said, 'Today it is going to rain.'

I looked up. It was a clear sky. I said, 'What nonsense! Where is the rain?'

He said, 'No, swami, it *will* rain today.'

And it *did* rain that day.

Then I sat up for days and nights. Why couldn't I feel what this man could feel? I sat, holding my hand in different positions, trying to feel the moisture, the temperature, trying to read the sky. I read all kinds of meteorological books, but it felt like I was up against a wall. But then, with careful observation of my own body and what was around, I discovered the most fundamental mistake that most of us make: the fact that we view the ingredients which constitute our body, like earth, water, air, food and fuel, as commodities and not as an essential part of the life process.

After about eighteen months of trying really hard, I understood. And now if I say it is going to rain, ninety-five per cent of the time it will rain. This is not magic, but the minute observation of a completely different level of your own system, of the earth, of the air that you breathe, of everything around you. If it is to rain today, some change will happen in your body. Most urban-dwellers cannot feel it, but many rural people do, unknowingly. Most insects, birds and animals can feel it.

Recognizing these small changes in the planetary system, people of the past tried to make use of them for their own spiritual growth. Do you know that the magnetic equator of the planet flows through India? A few thousand years ago, our ancients found the exact location and built a whole string of temples along the magnetic equator. One of the most famous temples is the Chidambaram temple. Many spiritual seekers gathered there over the centuries at times when the planet was in a certain position. In this temple, a shrine is consecrated to 'nothingness' or 'zero', indicating the zero degree of magnetic play upon the planet and its impact on all the lives around.

This is not mere symbolism but a powerful device to liberate oneself literally from the ways of the world.

This is one kind of spiritual system. Another system, of meditativeness, completely ignores the simple changes that happen in creation and focuses on absorbing the self into the source of creation. These are the two fundamental ways – you can either go slowly, step-by-step, or you can ignore all the steps and take the leap. One makes involvement mandatory; another entails withdrawal from the situations in which we exist. You can choose whichever is suitable for you. In the times in which we live, a balance between the two is best.

THE NEXT STEP

The moment it is in touch with the earth, the body recognizes it.

That is why spiritual people in India walked barefoot and always sat upon the ground in a posture that allows for maximum area of contact. In this way, the body is experientially reminded that it is just a part of this earth. Never should the body forget what it is. If it forgets, it will start making fanciful demands; if you constantly remind it, then it knows its place.

If you tend to fall sick very easily, just sleep on the floor (or with something only minimally between you and the floor). It will make a big difference. Also, sit closer to the ground. Every day for just half an hour go sit in your garden, on the ground, quietly. You will find your health improving dramatically.

In Sync with the Sun

'If you are very compulsive, you will see that situations, experiences, thoughts and emotions will be cyclical.'

Surya Namaskar simply means to bow down to the sun in the morning. Why is this traditional sequence of postures practised in yoga?

The sun is the life source for this planet. In everything that you eat, drink and breathe, there is an element of the sun. Only if you learn how to better digest the sun, internalize it, and make it a part of your system, do you truly benefit from this process.

Generally people understand Surya Namaskar as an exercise: it strengthens your back, your muscles, etc. Yes, it definitely does do all that and more, but that is not the objective. Surya Namaskar is essentially about building a dimension within you where your physical cycles are in sync with the sun's cycles, which run about twelve and a quarter years. It is not by accident but by intent that it has been structured with twelve postures. If your system is at a certain level of vibrancy and readiness, and in a good state of receptivity, then naturally your cycle will be in sync with the solar cycle.

Young women have an advantage – although a lot of them turn it into a disadvantage – in that they are also in sync with the lunar cycles. It is an advantage, but a lot of them treat it as a curse – as 'PMS'. It is a fantastic possibility that your body is connected to both the solar cycle and to the lunar cycle. Nature has granted this advantage to a woman because she has been entrusted with the extra responsibility of propagating the human race. So she has been given some extra privileges. In the past, many women who came in sync with lunar cycles became highly intuitive; they learnt to perceive with much less effort what others can only dream of. Unfortunately, today people don't know how to handle the extra energy that is generated at that time and hence treat it as a curse and even a kind of madness, as evinced by the word 'lunar' turning into 'loony'.

Being in sync with the solar cycle is an important part of balance and receptivity, a means of taking the body to the edge, so that it is not a hurdle. The physical body is a fantastic stepping-stone for higher possibilities, but for most people it functions like a road block. The compulsions of the body do not allow them to go forward.

Between the menstrual cycle, which is the shortest cycle (a twenty-eight day cycle) and the cycle of the sun, which is over twelve years, there are many other kinds of cycles. The word 'cyclical' denotes repetition. Repetition means that in some way it is compulsive. Compulsiveness means it is not conducive

> Being in sync with the solar cycle is an important part of balance and receptivity.

for consciousness. Sadhana is always to ride the cycle so that there is no more compulsiveness, and you have the right kind of foundation for consciousness. In this way, a natural process becomes a process of liberation rather than entrapment.

The repetitive nature of cyclical movements or systems, which we traditionally refer to as *samsara*, offers the necessary stability for the making of life. If it were all random, it would not be possible to house a steady life-making machine. For the solar system and for the individual, being rooted in cyclical nature gives a certain firmness and steadiness of life. But once life has reached the level of evolution that human beings have reached, it is natural to aspire not just for stability, but for transcendence. Now, it is left to individual human beings to either remain trapped in the cyclical, which is the basis of stable physical existence, or to use these cycles for physical well being – to ride them and go beyond the cyclical.

If you are very compulsive, you will see that situations, experiences, thoughts and emotions will be cyclical. They keep coming back to you once in six months or eighteen months, three years or six years. If you just look back and see, you will notice this. If they come once in over twelve years, that means your system is in a good state of receptivity and balance. Surya Namaskar is an important process to enable that to happen.

So, this sequence of postures is a complete workout for the

physical system – a comprehensive exercise form without any need for equipment. But above all, it is an important tool that empowers human beings to break free from the compulsive cycles and patterns of their lives. Through practice if one attains a certain level of stability and mastery over the system, one could then be introduced to a more powerful and spiritually significant process called the Surya Kriya.

THE NEXT STEP

If you have a meticulous and conscientious mind, and an agile and balanced body, it will take you four to nine months with a good teacher to get the geometry of the Surya Kriya right. Once you get this right, the benefits are too immense to be listed. One of the most important effects is health and an immense sense of vitality.

Right Things for Wrong Reasons

'Swami used to do 1008 Surya Namaskars per day. Later on, after he was ninety years of age, he brought the number down to 108.'

Malladihalli is a village in northern Karnataka. Raghavendra Rao, my teacher, a legend in his lifetime, was generally known as Malladihalli Swami because he came from that village. When I first met him he was about seventy-nine years of age, and I was just eleven or twelve.

In the village where my grandfather lived there were wells in the backyard which were just six or seven feet in diameter and 120 or 130 feet deep. The water level would be somewhere between sixty to seventy feet below. One of my favorite sports was to jump into one of these wells and then climb up again. As these wells had no stairs, ladders or foot holes, coming up was quite a feat. I was pretty good at it. But if you made one mistake, your brains would become a smear on the wall.

One day when we were at it, an old man over seventy years of age was watching us. Without a word, he jumped into the well. I thought this was the end of him, but he came up faster than me! I didn't like it.

I kept my pride aside and asked him, 'How?'

He said, 'Come, do yoga.'

I just followed him like a puppy. That is how I got into yoga. And I am telling you this so you know: as long as you do the right thing even for the wrong reasons, it still works!

Malladihalli Swami was known to do 1008 Surya Namaskars per day. Later on, after he was ninety years of age, he brought the number down to 108 (not because he wasn't capable, but because there was no time). That was his sadhana. He lived almost like a superhuman being in nearly everything he did.

He was also a very wonderful Ayurvedic doctor. He was one of the few *nadi vaidyas* – by feeling your pulse he could diagnose your ailment. He would not only tell you what disease you had today, but he would predict what disease you were likely to get in the next ten to fifteen years, and would teach the remedial practices that you could do. Only one day in a week he would sit in his ashram as an Ayurvedic doctor. Wherever he was, he would travel back to the ashram on Sunday evening to be there on Monday morning. If he sat down at four o'clock in the morning, he was right there through the day till seven or eight o'clock in the evening. Volunteers would come in shifts to help him, but he himself sat there through the whole day. For every patient who came, he had a joke to tell. People would forget they had come for treatment. It was not like a doctor–patient interaction; it was like a festival.

This happened when he was about eighty-three years of age. One Sunday, late at night, he was in a railway station about seventy kilometres from his ashram. He was with two companions, and they discovered that the railways were on strike. This meant no trains and no other means of transport. His commitment to his work was such that he left his two companions on the platform and just ran seventy kilometres overnight on the railway track!

At four o'clock in the morning he was at the ashram, ready to treat his patients. People at the ashram did not even realize that he had come running. Only when the other two reached there, they told the others what Swamiji had done. That is how incredibly he lived.

Elemental Mischief

'The play of five elements is so complex; yet at the same time, the key is you.'

Life is a five-cornered game with just five ingredients. Whether it is the individual human body or the larger cosmic body, essentially it is made of five elements – earth, water, fire, air and space.

Even if you want to make *sambar*, you need seventeen ingredients, but here with just five ingredients, what a creation! When something seems phenomenally complex, and you dive into it and find out that it is just the juggling of five ingredients, it becomes a joke. So those who attained self-realization called it a cosmic joke.

Once, driving beyond midnight, I approached a mountain that I was supposed to go up. Then I saw, almost half the mountain was aflame! But I am not known to shy away from danger, so I continued to drive carefully, looking around me, because I was driving a car full of flammable fuel. It was misty and however far I went, the fire seemed to be a little farther away. Then I realized that although all the places that I saw from down below looked like

> If you have mastery over the elements, you not only have mastery over the body and over the mind, but over all of creation.

they were on fire, as I was actually driving to them, there was nothing at all.

Then I reached the actual site of the fire, and I saw a truck that had broken down. The driver and his two companions had built a small fire for themselves because it was cold. As the mist reached towards dew point, the million droplets in the air, each one acting as a prism, created such a phenomenal illusion that a little fire seemed like a major conflagration. From down below, it seemed like the whole mountain was aflame! That phenomenon left me astounded.

Creation is just like that, hugely magnified. If you look at this little piece of life – yourself – that is all it takes. Those who look within closely realize there is no need to look at the magnified version. The entire cosmos is just a magnified projection of a little thing that is happening within you – the play of five elements.

If you want to realize the full potential of this human mechanism or if you want to transcend it and merge with the larger cosmic mechanism – whether your desire is for the individual or the universal – you need a certain amount of mastery over these five elements. Without this mastery, you can neither know pleasure of the individual self nor the blissfulness of the cosmic being. If you know how to organize these five elements within yourself properly, then there is nothing more to life. Be it health, well being, perception, enlightenment, everything is taken care of.

The most fundamental practice in the yogic system is called *bhuta shuddhi*. '*Bhuta*' refers to the *pancha bhutas*, or the five elements. '*Shuddhi*' means to cleanse. If you learn to cleanse the five elements in the system, that's all there is. You now attain to what is called *bhuta siddhi*, which means you have mastery over the elements. If you have mastery over the elements, you not only have mastery over the body and mind, but over all of creation.

Every sadhana that you do has something to do with organizing these five elements in such a way that you can reap the best out of your being and cosmic nature. Whether your physical body becomes a stepping stone or a hurdle on the path of such mastery essentially depends on how you are able to deal with these five elements. What you are right now is just a little bit of earth, water, air, temperature and space. These few ingredients have come together to make a throbbing human being.

It is the mischief of these five elements which is your body. If they do not cooperate, then struggle as you might, nothing significant ever happens to you. Only with their cooperation does your life – from the basic to the highest aspects – become a possibility.

The body is like a doorway. A door has two aspects to it: if you are always facing closed doors, then for you a door means a deterrent; if doors are always opening up for you, then for you a door means a possibility of entry. It is the same door, but which side of it you are on decides everything about your life.

They say how long a minute is essentially depends on which side of the bathroom door you are! People who are inside say, 'Just a minute, I'm coming.' That one minute, for the person who is outside, is an eternity! Whether you experience this life as a great possibility or a great barrier simply depends on to what extent these five elements cooperate with you.

It once happened. A bishop was visiting New York City. He was to hold a meeting in Central Park, and all the Catholics were supposed to be there. Then, at the appointed time, they discovered that there were just a handful of Catholics in the city. They all came, and the bishop was talking to them about reaffirming their faith and spreading the message and increasing their numbers. Then one of the recent converts asked the bishop, 'Dear Father, why can't Jesus be born in New York City and reaffirm the faith once again?'

The bishop thought for a moment, and then he said, 'If Jesus has to be born, certain conditions have to be fulfilled, my son. One thing is we need three wise men, and that is not possible in New York City. And where will you find a virgin?'

If anything needs to happen we need the necessary ingredients and atmosphere for them to fall together. Bhuta shuddhi is a way of purifying the elements in the system in such a way that they cooperate.

Both the possibility and the bondage of life are through the five elements. Freedom and bondage are two edges of the same sword. If you swing it one way, it is freedom; if you swing it another way, bondage.

> Freedom and bondage are two edges of the same sword.

The whole life process is like this. Love and hate are encapsulated in each other; life and death are included in each other. If they were separate, you could have easily dealt with them, but they are always within each other. If you try to avoid death, you will end up avoiding life. Within yourself, if you just create this feeling of 'I don't want to die,' all that will happen is you will not step out of your bed. The only thing you will avoid is life, not death. This is the way life is – everything one inside the other. What is there is here, what is here is there. Above all, if you look at it, everything is just within you. It seems to be so complex; at the same time, it is absolutely simple.

In ancient India there were courtesans who were supposed to be masters in the art of seduction. They wore elaborate jewellery, where the whole body would be covered in ornaments. There was no way to take these off. If you had to take them off one by one, it would take a long time. The man, fired up by lust, would want to undress this woman, but he would not be able to take these off. She would go on encouraging him with a little more liquor or wine—a little more, a little more, and a little more. As his vision got a little more blurred, his task got even more difficult, and then soon, he just fell fast asleep, snoring. But there was just one pin; all it took was to just pull this one pin, and everything fell down. That only *she* would know.

Life is just like that. It is one complex web, but there is just one simple pin. If you pull that, everything will just fall. And that pin is *you*. If you know how to pull yourself out, suddenly everything settles. Everything is crystal clear. The play of five elements is highly complex; yet at the same time, the key is you. If you pull the plug it just collapses, and you are free.

The Next Step

The simplest thing that you can do to change the health and fundamental structure of your body is to treat the five elements with devotion and respect. Just try this. Every time you are consciously in touch with any of the elements, just refer to it as whatever you think of as the highest in your life, be it Shiva, Rama, Krishna, Jesus, Allah (or Marx!). You are a psychological being right now, and your mind is full of hierarchies. This process will settle the hierarchy. After some time, the word can fall off. But you will instantly see the change as the number of truly conscious moments in your life increase.

Pancha Bhuta

'These five temples were built so that they function as one system.'

In southern India, people who had the knowledge built five major temples for the five elements.

These temples were created not for worship but for a specific type of sadhana. To become free from the water element you would go to a particular temple and do one kind of sadhana. To become free from the element of air, you would go to another one; for water, another one. Like this, there are five wonderful temples for all the five elements which were infused with the kind of energy that assists that type of sadhana. Traditionally, yogis travelled from one temple to another continuing their sadhana. This is a land which has seen that kind of focus and understanding for a very long time.

The temples are referred to as the *Pancha Bhuta Sthalam*s. Geographically they are all within the Deccan Plateau. The temple in Kanchipuram is for earth; Thiruvanakaival for water; Thiruvannamalai for fire; Srikalahasti for air; and Chidambaram for space.

These five temples were built so that they function as one system. This is a phenomenal technology that allows those who know how to do the appropriate sadhana to visit the temple and make use of it. Those who do not know will benefit just by living in that region. Today, the connection between the five temples is absent. The sadhana and mastery over technology are difficult to find nowadays, but the temples still exist and many are magnificent pieces of architecture.

Body an Issue?

'Yoga pays so much attention to food because you are constructing the body with the food that you eat.'

It happened. One day in court the emperor Akbar asked, 'What do you think gives most pleasure to a man?'

There are all kinds of sycophants around emperors, so somebody said, 'Oh, my lord, serving you is the greatest pleasure in my life!'

Somebody else said, 'Just looking at your face is the highest pleasure I can have!'

Like this, the hyperbole poured forth. Birbal was just sitting there, bored.

Akbar asked, 'Birbal, you're not saying anything. What gives you maximum pleasure?'

Birbal said, 'Shitting.'

Till then, Akbar was feeling great with what people were

saying. Now he got really mad. He said, 'For uttering such an obscenity in the court, you had better prove it. If you can't prove it you are in danger.'

Birbal said, 'Give me a fortnight. I'll prove it to you.'

Akbar said, 'Fine.'

The next weekend, Birbal organized a hunting trip for Akbar into the forest, and he made sure all the women in the palace also travelled on this hunting trip. He set up the camp in such a way that Akbar's tent was in the centre, and all around, he placed the families, children and women. He told the catering department to produce the best food. They produced everything and Akbar ate well – he was on a vacation, you know!

The next morning when he got up and came out, there was no toilet tent. He went back into his tent and walked up and down, but the pressure was building up. He tried to go into the forest, but Birbal had made sure all the womenfolk were all over the place. He was not able to do it anywhere.

Pressure built up by the minute. It was about twelve noon, and he couldn't bear it any more. He was just about to burst, when Birbal, who was watching this whole scene, muttered, 'Toilet tent, where to put it, where to put it?' He was simply creating confusion and delaying it for another five to ten minutes.

The emperor was full of shit, and just when there was no more time left, they put up the toilet tent. Akbar went inside and moaned with relief. Then Birbal who was waiting for him outside the tent, asked, 'Do you agree with me now?'

Akbar said, 'It *is* the greatest pleasure.'

Relief from something that you cannot hold within you is

always the greatest pleasure, isn't it? Whatever that thing may be!

So, the body *can* become an issue. A big issue.

Your body is just a heap of food. Yoga pays so much attention to food because you are constructing your body with the food you eat. What kind of food you put into the system definitely has an impact on the kind of body you have. Are you preparing this body because you want to run as swiftly as a cheetah? Or are you preparing this body because you want to carry a hundred kilograms? Or are you preparing this body so that it becomes conducive for higher possibilities? You need to eat the right kind of food depending on your inclination and what you want out of your life.

THE NEXT STEP

It's important not to keep eating through the day. If you are below thirty years of age, three meals every day will fit well into your life. If you are over thirty years of age, it is best to reduce eating to two meals per day. Our body and brain work at their best only when the stomach is empty. So be conscious of eating in such a way that within two and a half hours your food moves out of the stomach, and within twelve to eighteen hours completely out of the system. With this simple awareness, you will experience much more energy, agility and alertness. These are the ingredients of a successful life, irrespective of what you choose to do with it.

Food as Fuel

'Don't ask your doctor, don't ask your nutritionist, don't ask your yoga teachers or anybody. Ask the body what kind of food it is most comfortable with.'

The way you eat not only decides your physical health, but the very way you think, feel and experience life. Trying to eat intelligently means understanding what kind of fuel this body is designed for and accordingly supplying that kind of fuel so that it functions at its best.

Let us say you bought a petrol car, but you pumped kerosene into it and drove it around. It might still move about, but it would not function at its optimal capacity, and its life could also be seriously affected. Similarly, if we do not understand what kind of fuel this body is designed for, if we just force whatever comes on to our plate into the system, it will definitely not function at its optimum level and even its lifespan can be reduced.   Compatibility of the fuel and of the machine is of great importance if you are seeking a certain calibre of function.

What kind of food is the human system really designed for?

If you eat certain foods, the body will become happy. If you eat certain other foods, the body will become dull and lethargic; it will increase your sleep quota. If you sleep for eight

> Eating intelligently means understanding what kind of fuel this body is designed for.

hours a day, and if you live for a hundred years, that means you have slept for thirty-three of those years. That means you have spent one-third of your life sleeping! Another thirty to forty per cent goes in eating, toilet and the other ablutions. There is very little time left for life.

So how do we keep the body well rested? First of all, why tire it? For most people, tiredness is not caused by work. Actually, most people who work more are also more active. Food is one important factor in keeping the body well rested. Attitudes also play a part, but food plays a major role.

You eat food for energy, but if you eat a big meal, do you feel energetic or lethargic? Depending upon the quality of the food that you eat, you first feel lethargy, and then slowly you start feeling energetic.

Why is this so?

One aspect is, your system cannot digest cooked food as it is; it needs certain enzymes. All the enzymes necessary for the digestive process are not present in the body alone; the food that you eat also brings these enzymes. When you cook the food, generally eighty to ninety per cent of the enzymes are destroyed. So the body is struggling to reconstitute these destroyed enzymes. The enzymes that you destroy in cooking can never be totally reconstituted, so generally, for most human beings, about fifty per cent of the food that they eat is going waste.

Another aspect is the stress on the system. To produce a small amount of energy, you have to eat so much food. The body has to process all this food just to get the quota of energy for your daily activity. If we ate foods with the necessary enzymes, the system would be functioning at a completely different level of efficiency and the conversion ratio of food to energy would be very different. Eating natural foods, in their live, uncooked condition, when the cells are still alive, will bring an enormous sense of health and energy.

One can easily experiment with this and see. Don't ask your doctor, your nutritionist, yoga teachers or anybody. When it comes to food, it is about the body. Ask the body what kind of food it is most comfortable with, not your tongue. The kind of food your body feels most comfortable with is always the ideal food to eat.

> As your body awareness evolves, you will know exactly what a certain food will do to you.

You must learn to listen to your body, if you want to understand the best food to eat. As your body awareness evolves, you will know exactly what a certain food will do to you. You do not even have to put it into your mouth. One can develop this kind of sensitivity that if you just look at or touch the food, you will know.

THE NEXT STEP

You can experiment: arrange the best possible meal for yourself, get angry with something, curse the whole world, and then eat it. You will see that day how food behaves within you. At the next meal, approach your food with reverence and eat it. You will now see how it behaves within you. (Of course, if you're sensible, you'll ignore the first and do only the second!)

Most people can bring down the quantum of food they are eating to a third and be much more energetic and not lose weight. It is just a question of how much receptivity you have created within yourself. Accordingly your body receives. If you can do the same amount of work, maintain all the bodily processes, with thirty per cent of the food that you eat, that definitely means you are running a much more efficient machine, doesn't it?

Hell's Kitchen

'There is nothing religious, philosophical, spiritual or moral about the food that we eat. It is only a question of whether the food is compatible with the kind of body that we have.'

There is an ongoing debate between the proponents of vegetarianism and non-vegetarianism. I am often asked which is better.

Vegetarians always act 'holier than thou', while non-vegetarians always claim they are more robust and fit for the world, as they treat all species on the planet as part of their menu. Huge philosophies have evolved based on choice of food. One must remember there is nothing religious, philosophical, spiritual or moral about the food that we eat. It is only a question of whether the food is compatible with the kind of body that we have.

This compatibility can be towards various ends. If being big is your highest aspiration, then certain types of foods have to be consumed. If you want a body that supports a certain level of intelligence, or a body with a certain level of alertness, awareness and agility, other types of foods must

> It is very important that this choice of what you eat is conscious – not simply led by the compulsion of the tongue but by the essential design of your body.

be consumed. If you want a body which is highly perceptive – if you are not someone who will settle just for health and pleasure of life but want to download the cosmos – you will need to eat in a very different way. For every aspiration that a human being has, accordingly he will have to manage his food; or if your aspirations involve all these dimensions, you will have to find a suitable balance.

Keeping aside our personal goals and aspirations, what type of fuel is this body designed for? This is something all of us should pay attention to first. Modifications, adjustments and adaptations of diet should come later. If it is a question of simply basic survival, eat whatever you want. But once survival is taken care of and there is a choice, it is very important that this choice of what you eat is conscious – not simply led by the compulsion of the tongue but by the essential design of our bodies.

If you observe the animal kingdom, you can largely classify

animals as herbivores and carnivores – those that eat vegetable matter and those that consume meat or prey upon other animals. Between these two categories of creatures, there are fundamental differences in the design and construction of their physical systems. Since we are focusing on food, let us explore the digestive system alone. The whole alimentary canal is a digestive trap from the lip to the anal outlet. If you travel down this tube, you will find some very fundamental differences between herbivores and carnivores. Let us look at a few significant ones.

If you look at the jaw movement of animals, you will find that carnivores have only a cutting function in their jaws, but the herbivores have both cutting and grinding functions. Obviously, we human beings have both cutting and grinding actions.

What is the reason for this design difference?

Suppose you take a bit of uncooked rice and place it in your mouth for a minute or more – you would notice it turns sweet. This sweetness is happening because right there in your mouth carbohydrates are getting converted into sugar (an essential part of the digestive process) by an enzyme called ptyalin which is in your saliva. Ptyalin is present in the saliva of all herbivores, but not carnivores. So carnivores just have to cut their food into smaller pieces and swallow, but herbivores have to chew their food. Mastication involves grinding and then thoroughly mixing the food with saliva. Hence the design modification in the jaw.

If mastication happens properly, close to fifty per cent of your digestive process should be completed in the mouth. In other words, the stomach is expecting partially digested food to efficiently complete the process. As these days most foods are fairly overcooked, you tend to swallow the food quickly without the needed mastication, which constantly burdens the stomach with not only undigested food but also partially destroyed food. Today's kitchens have largely become places where you efficiently destroy food. Food that is nutritious and full of life is systematically destroyed through the cooking process, which depletes its nutritional value and largely obliterates its *pranic* value (or its capacity to be spiritually supportive).

Next, if you look at the length of the alimentary canal, for herbivores it is generally about twelve to sixteen times the length of their body. In carnivores, it ranges from two to five times the length of their body. To put it simply, carnivores have distinctly shorter alimentary canals compared to herbivores, and this difference clearly indicates what type of food an individual species is supposed to consume.

In your present system if you eat raw meat, it would take anywhere between 70 to 72 hours to pass through; cooked meat will take 50 to 52 hours; cooked vegetables 24 to 30 hours; uncooked vegetables 12 to 15 hours; fruits 1 ½ to 3 hours.

If you keep raw meat outside for 70 to 72 hours, you know the level of putrefaction that happens – one small piece of meat can evict you from your home! Putrefaction occurs very rapidly in the summer time, when the temperature and moisture is conducive. Your stomach is always a tropical place, and if meat stays there for up to 72 hours, the level of putrefaction is very high. This essentially means there is excessive bacterial activity in your body, and it has to expend a lot of energy to ensure that the bacterial level does not cross the tipping point from health to illness.

If you go to visit a friend who is sick in hospital, you would surely not take him mutton biryani or steak. You would have the sense to take fruit. If you happen to be in the wild, what would be the first thing you would eat? Definitely fruit. Then would come roots, the killing of an animal, cooking and raising crops. Fruit is the most easily digestible food.

Most carnivorous animals do not eat every day – definitely not three times a day! They know the food they eat moves very slowly through their digestive tracts. A tiger is said to eat once in six to eight days. He is agile and prowling when he is hungry, eats a hefty meal of twenty-five kilograms at one go, and then generally sleeps or ambles around lazily. The alert and perky creatures you see in the wild are always herbivores. They keep eating through the day. A cobra eats sixty per cent of its own body weight in a single meal, and eats only once in twelve to fifteen days. The pygmies from the central African region used to hunt elephants, eat their organs and meat raw and drink the blood fresh. They say they would sleep after this kind of meal for over forty hours at a stretch. But you cannot afford this sort of lifestyle. You have to eat every day and rest at specific times, as your alimentary canal is similar to that of herbivores.

Protein Debate

There is much emphasis laid nowadays on eating protein. It's important to understand that only three per cent of our body is composed of protein and excess protein consumption could cause cancer. Meat is high in protein. But a very small portion of the meat that one consumes can fulfil this protein requirement. However, it also travels very slowly through the alimentary canal, leads to a variety of problems from excessive bacterial activity, enhanced sleep quota, and increased inertia levels in the body as a whole, to decreased cellular regeneration. All of this in turn manifests as a drop in one's sensitivity of perception. It is in this context that meat has been regarded as spiritually unsupportive—essentially because the spiritual process is about enhancing one's perception beyond the limitations of the physical.

Digestion Drama

'Your problem is not enough attention but too much information.'

Another important aspect of food we need to remember is that to digest certain kinds of food the digestive system produces alkalis, and to digest a different set of food it generates acid. If you consume a jumble of foods, then the stomach becomes confused and produces both acids and alkalis which neutralize each other and make digestive juices lose their edge. Hence the food will remain in the stomach region longer than required, and weakens our ability to rejuvenate on the cellular level. It also causes what we refer to as *tamas,* or inertia in the energy system, which over a period of time will alter the very quality of who you are and impair the quality of who you could be.

Traditionally, in southern India, people took care never to mix certain foods. But today, food is no more about the well being of the body, but a social affair. When people eat at buffets, the variety of food served is considered more important than nourishing the body.

The question is not about what *not* to eat but about how *much* of *what* to eat. It is not a moral issue; it is a question of life sense. As you battle city life, you need an agile mind, and physical and mental balance. And some of you also have spiritual aspirations (even if it is only every once in a while!). So every individual must arrive at his or her own balance of diet, not by taking vows, but by observation and awareness.

> Every individual must arrive at his or her own balance of diet, not by taking vows, but by observation and awareness.

It is important not to turn into a food freak. Food should never become an all-consuming affair. Every creature on the planet knows what to eat and what not to. What is your problem then? Your problem is not enough attention but too much information.

THE NEXT STEP

The consumption of a spoonful of ghee (clarified butter) on a daily basis a few minutes before a meal does wonders for the digestive system. If you eat ghee with sugar, as in sweets, it is digested and turns into fat. But ghee without sugar can cleanse, heal and lubricate the alimentary canal. Additionally, the cleansing of the colon will immediately manifest as a certain glow and aliveness to your skin.

Fishy Wisdom

'Among the animals, fish, being one of the earlier forms of life upon this planet, have the easiest software code for our system to break and integrate into ourselves.'

If you must eat non-vegetarian food, the best would be fish. Firstly, it is easily digestible with very high nutritional values. Secondly, it leaves the least amount of its imprint upon you.

What is meant by this?

All that we eat, all that we carry as our body, what we excrete and what gets eventually cremated, is just earth, earth and earth. The software within your system determines that if you eat a banana it is transformed into human flesh and a human body – not a monkey or a mouse. The efficiency of your system obliterates the other software that transformed soil into a banana and arrives at a new software that will make a banana into a human form. For more evolved creatures, particularly mammals, their software is more distinct and individuated. This makes it harder for your code-breaking system to obliterate the software of the creature that you consume and to overwrite it with a new software. Hence, you slowly begin to acquire the character of that creature.

Among the animals, fish, being one of the earlier forms of life upon this planet, have the easiest software code for our system to break and integrate into ourselves. Animals which have more intelligence and particularly those which are capable of a variety of emotions (like cows or dogs) will retain their own memory systems. In other words, we are incapable of completely integrating more evolved, intelligent, and emotionally endowed creatures.

Conscious Eating

'Fasting is not to torture yourself; it is to become free from the torture chamber that your body can very easily become.'

If you observe the natural cycle of the body, you will find there is something called a *mandala*. A mandala is a cycle of forty to forty-eight days which the system goes through. In every cycle, there will be three days where your body does not need food. If you are conscious of how your body functions, you will become aware that on a particular day the body does not require food. Without effort you can go without food on that day. Even dogs and cats have this awareness; on a particular day they will not eat.

The day the system says 'no food' is a clean-up day. Since most people do not have the awareness of which day their body should go without food, the day of Ekadashi was fixed. Ekadashi is the eleventh day of the lunar segment and happens every fourteen days. It is a day to fast. If some people are unable to go without food because their activity levels are such and they do not have appropriate sadhana to support their system, they can go on a fruit diet.

> If you are conscious of how your body functions, you will become aware that on a particular day the body does not need food.

If you force yourself to fast without preparing your body and mind sufficiently, you will only cause damage to your health. But if your body is properly prepared, and if you are mentally in a certain state, fasting can be of much benefit.

People who are constantly drinking coffee and tea will find that fasting can become very difficult. So before fasting, prepare the body by eating the right kind of foods. It may not be a good thing for everybody to fast, but it has many benefits if done with proper understanding.

My mother used to do this: every day before she ate her breakfast, she would take one handful of it and go looking for the ants and feed all of them. Only then would she eat. This has been a tradition among the womenfolk in many families. An ant is the smallest thing you can see around, the most inconsequential thing in people's minds. So, you first feed the ant – not the elephant, or the gods, or other celestial creatures. You feed the smallest creature. He has as much of a right to eat as you have; this planet belongs as much to him as it belongs to you. You understand that every creature on this planet has the same right to live as you have. This awareness creates a conducive atmosphere, mentally and physically, for consciousness to grow.

Just a simple act like this loosens you from your body. It brings awareness that you are not the body. As you become less of a body, your awareness of the other dimensions of who you are naturally becomes enhanced. When you are very hungry all your body wants to do is eat. Just wait for two minutes; you will find that it will make a big difference. When you are very hungry you *are* the body. Give it a little space and suddenly you are not just a body.

Gautama the Buddha went to the extent of saying, 'When you are badly in need of food, if you give away your food to somebody else, you will become stronger.' I am not going that far; I am only saying, just wait a few minutes! It will definitely leave you stronger. If you are very compulsive about food it is good to miss one meal consciously. Try saying this to yourself: 'Today I am very hungry, and all my favorite dishes are being cooked. Today is the day I have decided to skip my meal.' This is not to torture yourself; this is to become free from the torture chamber that your body can very easily become.

What kind of food you eat, how much you eat, how you eat, turning it from a compulsive pattern into a conscious process, is the essence of fasting.

The Next Step

Just experiment. Start with 25 per cent natural, uncooked or live food—fruit and vegetables—today and slowly push it up to 100 per cent in about four or five days. Stay there for a day or two and again cut it down by 10 per cent and in another five days you will reach 50 per cent natural food, 50 per cent cooked food. This is ideal for most people, who wish to be active for sixteen or eighteen hours a day.

Remember, if you eat cooked food, you may be eating a meal in fifteen minutes. If you eat natural or uncooked food, you take a little more time to eat the same quantum of food, because you have to chew it a little more. But the nature of the body is such that after fifteen minutes it will tell you the meal is over. So people tend to eat much less, lose weight and think raw food is not good for them. You just need to be a little more conscious of how much you are eating.

Restlessness to Restfulness

'What the body needs is not sleep; what the body needs is restfulness.'

The fact that you sleep at night makes some difference between your mornings and evenings. Suppose you do not sleep well tonight, tomorrow morning will be bad. What is making the difference is the level of relaxation. If you could remain relaxed through the day, then you would be the same person in the evening that you were in the morning.

If your morning is good, that is a good beginning, but gradually during the day, you become stressed, your relaxation levels come down, you begin to lose your cool. Stress is not because of work – this must be understood. Everybody thinks their job is stressful. *No* job is stressful; it is your inability to handle your own system that is stressing you out. Somewhere, you do not know how to handle your body and mind, that is the problem.

How do you keep your system free of stress so that morning or evening you are at the same level of enthusiasm, relaxation, happiness?

You cannot slow down your system at the cost of activity. What is necessary is to keep your system in such a way that it gets relaxed by itself, that activity does not take a toll on it. Maybe physically you get exhausted, but this need not make you feel stressed in any way. If you are capable of being vigorous and still relaxed, then it is worthwhile. There is a whole technology for making this happen. You can find this out for yourselves: if you start certain simple practices of yoga, in three to four months' time, your pulse rate will drop at least eight to twenty counts very easily. That means the body is running so much more efficiently and at a relaxed pace.

What the body needs is not sleep but restfulness. If you keep the body very relaxed through the day, your sleep quota will go down naturally. If work is also a form of relaxation for you, if taking a walk or exercising is also relaxation for you, you will see your sleep quota will drop even further.

Right now, people want to do everything the hard way. I see people walking in the park in a state of tension. Whether you walk or jog, why can't you do it easily, joyfully? This exercise may be causing more harm to you than well being, because you are going at everything like it is a war.

Don't battle with life. You are not anti-life; you *are* life. Just get in tune with life and you will see that you will pass through

> Don't battle with life.
> You are not anti-life;
> you *are* life.

it easily. Keeping yourself fit and well is not a battle. Do some activity that you enjoy: play a game, swim, walk, whatever. If you don't like to do anything except eat potato chips, then there will be a problem! Otherwise, there is no problem about being relaxed with activity.

How much sleep does your body need? It depends on the level of physical activity you are performing. There is no need to fix either food or sleep. 'This many calories I must eat; this many hours I should sleep' – this is a foolish way to handle life. Let the body decide how much it should eat today, not you. Today your activity levels are low, so you eat less. Tomorrow your activity is very high, so you eat more. Similarly with sleep: when you feel sufficiently relaxed you come awake. The moment the body is rested it will wake up – maybe at three, maybe four, or maybe eight o'clock, it does not matter. Your body need not wake up to an alarm bell.

If you keep the body at a certain level of alertness and awareness you will see that once it is well rested, it will wake up. That is, if it is eager to come to life. If it is somehow trying to use the bed as a grave, then it is a problem. Keep the body in such a way that it is not longing to avoid or escape life; keep it in such a way that it is longing to come awake.

THE NEXT STEP

An average person's pulse rate on an empty stomach would be in the seventies or even eighties. For a person doing the right type of sadhana and who is meditative, the pulse rate would range between the thirties and forties. Even after a good lunch it would stay in the fifties. This is just one parameter that indicates the level of restfulness that your body is experiencing moment to moment. Restfulness essentially defines the replenishing and rejuvenating capability of the body. Stress is your inability to manage this. You can check out your pulse before and after meals and see for yourself.

Carnal to Cosmic

'You don't have to make biology sacred. Nor do you have to make it filthy. It is just there; it is the instrument of life.'

Existence is a dance between the unmanifest and manifest. The moment it manifests, there is duality. In the unmanifest there is unity. Though unity is the basic fabric of creation, duality brings texture, design and colour. All the various manifestations that you see as life today are fundamentally rooted in duality. Because there are two, there are many. There are many manifestations: light and darkness, male and female, life and death. If there was only one, there would be just existence. Once there are two, the game of life begins.

Once duality begins, sex begins. What we call sex is just two parts of this duality striving to become one. In the process of these dualities meeting, there are also certain functions that Nature wants to fulfil, like procreation and survival of the species.

This longing to become one finds expression in many ways. When you are young and your intelligence is hijacked by your hormones, sex will be the way. When you are middle-aged and your intelligence is hijacked by your emotions, love is the way. When you transcend all this, if you seek the same union in a much higher level of awareness, then yoga is the way.

If you are seeking oneness with the body, you need to remember that physical bodies will always remain two, no matter what you do. A few moments of a sense of unity will come, and then people fall apart. If divorce does not do it, death will. It is bound to happen.

The whole process of what we are referring to as sex is just two opposites making an attempt to become one. Your individuality means not only false boundaries that you have set up in your mental framework in the form of your likes and dislikes, loves and hates, etc.; it also means you are trapped within the boundaries of your own body. You may not be consciously aware of it, but the life within you is longing to break and go beyond these boundaries. When you want to break your mental boundaries you may long to have a serious conversation or read a book, drink alcohol, take a drug or do something freaky. To break your physical boundaries you may want to pierce yourself or get a tattoo, dye your hair, or go the old-fashioned way of sex.

The intention of sex is great, but the method is hopeless. Pleasure is involved, so it drives people towards each other,

> The intention of sex is great, but the method is hopeless.

but oneness never really comes. So you try to meet in other areas of emotion and intellect, you try to find some common ground – 'We like the same things, we like the same kind of ice cream, both of us are blond, both of us play Nintendo games, and both of us are fans of Harry Potter...' – people are always trying to find common ground. But unless you understand that you can never become one, you will not learn to enjoy the opposite.

These two energies, which in the human race we call 'man' and 'woman', are always trying to come together. At the same time, except for this longing to be together, they are opposites. They are lovers and enemies at the same time. If they look for similarities, there seems to be little common ground, but the attraction of the opposite is always there.

> To make a simple physical act beautiful, we have invented all kinds of decorations around it.

A lot of people cannot face the basic physical act as it is, so they have invented all kinds of decorations around it to make it beautiful. You always add emotion to the act, because without emotion it would feel ugly. In some way you are trying to cloud your vision of reality with decorations.

Sex is natural; it is there in the body. Sexuality is something you invented; it is psychological. If sex is in the body, it is fine, it is beautiful. The moment it enters your mind, it becomes a perversion – it has no business with your mind. Sex is a small aspect of you, but today it has become huge. For many, it has become life itself.

If you look at modern societies, I would say probably ninety per cent of human energy is being spent either pursuing or avoiding sex. We are trying to make this physical process many things that it is not. Sex is just nature's trick to reproduce. If this attraction of opposites did not exist, the species would become extinct. But now we have made such a distinction between man and woman, as if they are two separate species. No other creature on the planet has this kind of problem with sex as humans have. With animals, the urge is present in their body at certain times; otherwise they are free from it. With humans it is on their minds all the time.

One reason this has happened is that in the past, many religions went about denying a simple physical process to the extent of making it ugly. Because we could not even accept the biology of a human being, instead of looking beyond the limitations of the biological process, we tried to deny it.

Religion means liberation, doesn't it? How can there be liberation when you cannot even accept biology? If we had no problem with biology, everybody would be known for what they are worth. Whether somebody is a man or woman, what is the problem? When you cannot accept the physical differences between a man and a woman – that is where the whole exploitation of women starts.

You do not have to make biology sacred, nor do you have to make it filthy. It is the instrument of life, because of which you exist. If you know how to live it without decorating it or making it ugly, it has a beauty of its own.

THE NEXT STEP

The higher possibilities of life are housed in the human body. The physical body is a platform for all possibilities from the gross to the sacred. You can perform simple acts of eating, sleeping and sexuality as acts of grossness; or you can bring a certain dimension of sanctity to all these aspects. At its simplest, this sanctity can be achieved by bringing subtler thought, emotion and intention into these acts. And above all, the grossness and sanctity of something is largely decided by either your unwillingness and unconsciousness or willingness and consciousness. Every breath, every step, every simple act, thought or emotion, can acquire the stance of the sacred, if conducted recognizing the sanctity of the other involved – whether a person or a foodstuff or a thing that you use. Bring this sense of awareness into every simple act of your life.

Hormonal Hijack

'**Nothing wrong with your hormones, it is just that they
are causing compulsiveness. Compulsiveness means you
cannot determine what you want to be.**'

I am frequently asked why people are more obsessed with
sex than any other physical urge. I reply: it is just that your
intelligence has been hijacked by your hormones.

It is not you; it is just compulsive behaviour. When you
were a child, what your reproductive organs were did not really
matter. But the moment hormones started playing within you,
you could not think of the world beyond them. And you will see
after a certain age, when the play of hormones subsides, once
again it will not matter. You will look back and not believe you
were the one thinking about all that. There is nothing wrong
with the body; it is just limited. If you follow the way of the
body, it is not a crime; you may get some pleasure, but it will

> All life on this planet is just a recycling of the earth.

largely be an unfulfilled life.

Let us say tomorrow I grant you a boon and all the women or men in the world are after you, you will see that you will still not be satisfied. A little bit of pleasure and pain will happen. That is perfectly fine, but you will only live within the ambit of the body. The body knows only survival and procreation. And it is walking straight to the grave every moment, nowhere else.

Your body is just a loan from this planet. What you call 'death' is just Mother Earth reclaiming the loan that she offered to you. All life on this planet is just a recycling of the earth. If all that you have known is the body – and anyway you are going to lose all of it – fear becomes your constant companion. People are even beginning to think that fear is a natural part of one's existence. No. Fear is a *consequence* of the unnaturalness of your existence. That is, you have not explored life in its full depth and dimension, but you have limited yourself to the physical body because of which fear is a natural consequence.

Ever heard of George Best? He was one of the greatest footballers. He went all out to live his life. They described him as having every popular film star and model on his arm at some time or the other. Sometimes he had three at a time on his arm! But by the time he crossed thirty-five, he was such a broken, miserable, frustrated man, and by the age of fifty-nine, he was dead. He supposedly had everything but lived a terrible life.

That is because the way of the body is limited. The truth is the body has only so much of a role to play in your life. If you try to stretch it to all of your life, you will suffer because you are trying to create a falsehood. Life has its ways to bend you, break you, knead you and grind you in a million most unexpected ways.

For many, wealth and physical well being only drives them to do more and more desperate actions to achieve happiness. If you look under the cloak of civilization you will uncover most abominable forms of abuse. We are not even sparing our own children. These are consequences of a humanity not attending to all dimensions of a human being and addressing only the physical.

The desperation comes because you are trying to make a small aspect of your life everything. It will not work. Today, especially in attempting to make the body into everything, people are creating untold suffering. You cannot think of a better arrangement physically – healthcare, insurance, cars; you have more comforts and conveniences than any other generation ever. But people are suffering immensely. In affluent societies almost every fifth person is on some kind of medication just to maintain mental balance. When you have to take a tablet every day to remain sane, this is not joyfulness. You are on the verge of breaking down every day because you have made a small aspect of your life the whole of life. Life is just taking its toll, nothing else.

Mortality is the Key

'One who has not realized his eternal nature must at least realize his mortal nature.'

Only when you realize the mortal nature of who you are do you want to know what is beyond this. Only then the spiritual process opens up in your life.

This happened. Two men, who were over eighty years of age, met. Looking at the last name, one guy recognized the other and said, 'Did you go to war in World War II?'

The other man said, 'Yes.'

He asked him which place, which battalion. The other man told him.

Then, 'Oh, my God! Don't you recognize me? We were in the same foxhole!'

Oh, they hit it off! They talked and talked. All they actually saw was about forty minutes of an intense combat situation. They talked about every bullet that went by, *zing, zing*, just missing them by inches. About those forty minutes they spoke for over four hours.

When they exhausted everything that they could say about those forty minutes, one asked the other, 'Okay, since the war, what have you been doing?'

'Oh, these sixty years, I've just been a salesman.'

All their life, those forty minutes have been the most profound experience of their life. They could discuss it for hours and hours because mortality was hanging right in front of them at every moment. When mortality was so close, they made a bond that was profound. After that, this man was just a salesman.

Profoundness will enter you if you realize the mortal nature of who you are. One who has not realized his eternal nature must at least realize his mortal nature. Only when he realizes his mortal nature and confronts it, does the longing to go beyond become a genuine force. Otherwise all spiritual process is just bad entertainment.

Desire Is Life

'Unleash your desire; do not limit it to the limited. In the boundlessness of the desire is your ultimate nature.'

The question of desire has created much confusion because you have been told you must give up desire. You *want* to give up your desire: is that not a desire? Or if you say, 'I want to attain God' – is that not a very greedy desire? If somebody just desires a small piece of creation, you call that greed. If somebody wants the very Creator, is that not the ultimate greed? Most people are just looking for small pieces of creation. Someone is looking for the Creator himself; that is a most ambitious desire.

If you create a desire to give up your desire, you are still in desire. Have you ever seen anybody who has no desire? Can you imagine somebody without desire? Maybe they have different kinds of desires than you, but is there somebody who has no desire? There is no such thing, because the energy that you call 'life' and the energy that you call 'desire' are not different. No desire means really there is no possibility for life.

Any teaching which is not viable is not a teaching; it is just nonsense. Only if there is a possibility, you can call it a teaching. Utter nonsense has been spoken for so long. Just because something is printed in a book or somebody says it is holy, it does not become right, nor does it become true.

This teaching of desirelessness and detachment has come because people chose to involve themselves in a selective way with life. It has caused much confusion to them and to everybody around them. People are always saying, 'Give up attachment and be detached.' If you remain detached from life, would you know life? The only way to know life is through involvement.

The basis for all these teachings of detachment is the fear of entanglement. A large segment of the population is entangled in something or other, and because entanglement always creates pain and suffering, somebody came up with this foolish solution: 'Be detached.' This means their solution for life is: 'Avoid it.'

You are afraid of involvement; you think that if you are involved, you could get hurt. It is not so. If you are involved, you will not get hurt. Selective engagement with life leads to entanglement or what is normally referred to as attachment. When you choose to engage selectively with life, naturally, you get entangled with the process of life. It is the entanglement which causes the pain and suffering. People have generally known only entanglement, not involvement. If there is a possibility of pain, definitely you would hesitate to get involved.

But when there is no fear of entanglement that is when you would throw yourself into everything.

But without involvement there is no life. Whether it is the food that you eat, the people around you, the life around you, art, music, or whatever else – can you experience it without involvement? If you want to avoid life, it means death. Being alive and wanting to die but not dying is a torture. It is a half life.

> Without involvement there is no life.

The fundamentals of either enjoying or suffering the process of life are just this: if you are into anything willingly, that is your heaven; if you are into anything unwillingly, that is your hell. Whenever you are forced to do something that you do not desire you suffer that process.

What is most beautiful can become ugly if it happens to you unwillingly. The moment you say, 'I want to be detached,' you are making yourself unwilling to face the process of life, and you make a hell for yourself. People who have made a complete hell out of themselves, invariably, make a hell out of the world also – sometimes with very good intentions.

You would have heard of mythological stories where there were demons that had the capability to multiply themselves when a god or goddess attempted to eliminate them. For every drop of their blood that fell on the ground, a thousand demons would be born. These are not facts; these are dialectical expressions for the many demons that torment you from within. Your desires and passions are just like this: if you try and fight with them, if you chop them, they will spill blood, and with every drop, a hundred or a thousand will come up. You do not have to overcome desire, because desire is not an enemy. Desire is the basis of your existence. When desire causes misery, you start thinking that desire may be your adversary, but it is not so. Desire is what is making your life.

So, what to do with your desires?

Fighting them will be futile. Desire the highest in life. All your passions, just direct them to the highest possibility that you can think of. Educate your desires to flow in the right direction; that is all.

Desire is a tool towards your infinite nature, beyond all that is limited. The infinite cannot be approached in instalments. If the boundlessness of your desire finds expression in stages, it is a self-defeating process – an endless run, as you can never count yourself to infinity. Unleash your desire; do not limit it to the limited. In the boundlessness of the desire is your ultimate nature.

MIND

Clown as Gymnast

'Once the space between you and the activity of the mind grows, the mind is no more a mess. It is a great symphony; it is a tremendous possibility.'

In recent times, much work has gone into studying the activity of the mind, or more specifically, the brain. If you look at the way the neurons are firing in the brain, there is a tremendous cohesiveness in this activity. It is this cohesiveness which translates into the efficient functioning of the body. A billion things are happening in the body right now because of the extremely coordinated dance of neurons.

But the mind, in most people's experience, has unfortunately become a mess – a circus. A circus is actually a very coordinated activity, deliberately made to look like a mess. Even the clown in the circus is a gymnast. He is hugely talented and coordinated in what he does, but he is made to look like a clown.

How we conduct this circus is the whole point. Why has the mind – which is the most miraculous possibility in our lives – also become a misery-manufacturing machine?

Let us look at it this way. When do you feel well? When you are happy and joyful, isn't it? Even if you are medically ill, when you are joyful, you still feel well. So, well being essentially means that you are feeling pleasant within yourself. If your body feels pleasant, we call this health; if it becomes very pleasant, we call this pleasure. If your mind feels pleasant, we call this peace; if it becomes very pleasant, we call this joy. If your emotions feel pleasant, we call this love; if they become very pleasant, we call this compassion. If your life energies become pleasant, we call this bliss; if they become very pleasant, we call this ecstasy. This is all that every human being is seeking, isn't it?

If I meet you when you are feeling very pleasant, you are a wonderful and generous human being. This is true of every person. But if I happen to meet you when you are miserable or frustrated, you are invariably nasty. When you are feeling very pleasant within yourself, you express pleasantness. When you are feeling unpleasant within yourself, you express unpleasantness. What you want for your neighbour may be debatable, but what you want for yourself is the highest level of pleasantness, always!

So, essentially every human being is seeking pleasantness, within and without. When it comes to the outside, there are a million ingredients. Nobody has complete mastery over them. We can manage the outside situations. But we can *create* them only to some extent. Neither in the family, nor in work, nor in the larger world can you ever have situations hundred per cent the way you want. If it happens your way fifty-one per cent, you are doing great; you have the controlling stake. But when it comes to the inner situation, there is only one ingredient: *you.* At least you must happen the way you want. The world not happening your way is not the problem. If you were happening the way you wanted, you wouldn't cause misery to yourself, for sure. You would simply envision and create higher states of pleasantness within yourself.

'Why is it that I am not the way I want myself to be?' Simply because the fundamental faculties within you are not taking instructions from you.

Once this happened. A lady went to sleep. In her sleep she had a dream. In her dream she saw a hunk of a man staring at her. He started coming closer and closer. She could even feel his breath. She trembled . . . not in fear. And then she asked, 'What will you do to me?'

The man replied, 'Well lady, it's your dream!'

What is happening in your mind is your bloody dream, isn't it? Now, the problem is not that life is not happening the way you want it; even your dream is not happening the way you want it!

Right now the main problem is that your own mind is not working the way you want it. We are hoping the outside situation will fix it for us, but these things have to be fixed from within. Both

> Every kind of misery that human beings are going through is manufactured in their mind.

joy and misery come from within you; they never rain upon you from the outside. It just depends on the way you react to external stimuli. Instead of *acting* from within, you are *reacting* to outside situations, and hence unpleasantness wells up within you. Every kind of misery that human beings are going through is manufactured in their mind.

The whole system of yoga is just a technology to create a distinction between you and your mind. Once the space between you and the activity of the mind grows, the mind is no more a mess. It is a great symphony, a tremendous possibility, which can take you to great heights.

Yoga means to move towards an experiential reality where one knows the ultimate nature of existence, the very way that it is made. Yoga refers to union as an experience, not as an idea, philosophy, or concept that you imbibe. As an intellectual idea, if you vouch for the oneness of the universe, it may make you popular at a tea party, or give you a certain social status. You may even get a Nobel Prize. But it does not serve any other purpose.

It can actually cause damage to the individual to see everything as one, intellectually. People end up doing all kinds of silly things until somebody teaches them a good lesson. Things don't have to reach a point of life and death; you will see even, when it is just about money, the boundary is clear: 'This is me, that is you.' At such times, there is no question of you and I being one!

Once it happened. Shankaran Pillai went to a Vedanta class. The teacher was in full swing: 'You are not this; you are everywhere; there is nothing like "yours" and "mine";

everything is yours. What you see, hear, smell, taste, touch is not reality – it's all maya, illusion; everything is one.'

This sank deeply into Shankaran Pillai. He went and slept over the Vedanta. He got up in the morning, totally fired up. Usually he loved to sleep, but because of this Vedanta, now, first thing in the morning he started thinking, 'There is nothing here which is not mine. Everything is mine; everything is me. All that is in this world is me, and everything is maya.'

You know, whatever may be your philosophy, hunger comes. So he went to his favourite restaurant, ordered a big breakfast, and ate, saying to himself, 'The food is also me, I am also the food; the one who serves is also me, the one who eats is also me.' Vedanta!

> Yoga refers to union as an experience, not as an idea, philosophy, or concept that you imbibe.

He finished his breakfast, and with his stomach full, he looked around. He saw the owner of the restaurant sitting there. 'It's all mine, what is mine is yours, what is yours is mine.' With the same Vedanta going on, he got up and started walking out. When everything is yours, where is the question of paying the bill?

Just when he happened to cross the counter where the cash box was placed, the owner was distracted by some other work and went out. Now Shankaran Pillai saw a huge heap of currency in the till. Immediately, the Vedanta told him, 'Everything is yours; you cannot differentiate between this and that.' So since his pockets were quite empty, he put his hand into the box, took some money, stuffed it in his pocket and carried on walking, He was not out to rob anybody; he was just practising Vedanta.

A few people from the restaurant ran after him and caught him. Shankaran Pillai said, 'What are you going to catch? What you catch is also you; the one that catches is also you. What is in my stomach is also in your stomach, so whom can I pay?'

The owner was bewildered! All he knows is *idli, dosa, vada*! If a thief tries to run away, he knows how to catch him and thrash him. But when Shankaran Pillai said, 'The one who catches is also me, the one who is caught is also me,' he didn't know what to do. So he took him to court.

There, Shankaran Pillai continued his Vedanta. The judge tried in many ways to make him understand, but it was no good. Then the judge said, 'Okay, sixty lashes.'

First lash…reality hit.

Second lash… a shout.

Third lash…a scream.

Then the judge said, 'Don't worry, the one who lashes is also you, the one who is lashed is also you, so who can lash anybody? It's all maya. So sixty lashes on the backside.'

Now Shankaran Pillai cried, 'Please, no more Vedanta. Leave me alone!'

So, when you understand everything intellectually, it only leads to these deceptive states. But if oneness becomes an experiential reality, it will not bring forth any immature action. It will bring forth a tremendous experience of life.

If you try to stop the mental nonsense, you will go insane, because with your mind, all the three pedals are throttles;

there are no brakes, no clutch, nothing. Have you noticed this? Whatever you try to do, the mind only goes faster. But if you don't pay any attention to it, your thoughts will slowly dwindle away.

Individuality is an idea. Universality is not an idea; it is a reality. In other words, yoga means you bury all your ideas. Yoga is simply '*chitta vritti nirodha.*' That is, if the activity of your mind ceases and you are still alert, you are in yoga.

The Next Step

Remind yourself at least once an hour that everything you're carrying – your handbag, your money, your relationships, the heaviness in your heart and your body – are things you've accumulated over a period of time. If you become more and more conscious of this fundamental fact and a process of disidentification grows within you – balanced by a deep sense of involvement in everything – you will move from madness to meditation.

Honing the Blade

'The intellect is a wonderful instrument for survival; at the same time, the intellect is a terrible barrier that does not allow you to experience the oneness of life.'

If you look at it on the surface, we could divide the mind into three parts: the discriminatory dimension of the mind, which is the intellect; the accumulative dimension of the mind, which gathers information; and the third dimension, which is called *pragna* or awareness.

The first part is discriminatory. You are able to discriminate between a person and a tree only because your intellect is functioning. You know that you must walk through the door, not through the wall, only because your intellect is functioning. Without this dimension of discrimination, you would not know how to survive on this planet.

The nature of the discriminatory part of your mind is to

go on dividing everything. Modern education is essentially discriminatory in nature. So people went on splitting to a point where they split even the invisible atom. Once you let this intellect loose, it splits everything that it looks at; it does not allow you to *be* with anything totally. The intellect is a wonderful instrument for survival; at the same time, it is a terrible barrier that does not allow you to experience the oneness of life.

The intellect becomes a barrier because you keep it dipped in the accumulative part of the mind, or memory. You allow your intellect to function only with what you have accumulated till now. Let us look at this: every thought that arises in the mind is only coming from what you have already gathered. So when you keep the intellect dipped in the accumulative dimension of the mind, it loses its edge and becomes a trap. The same intellect can be sharpened if you awaken the other part of the mind – your awareness. Once the intellect is dipped in awareness, the discerning dimension of your mind will turn into a tool of liberation.

The accumulative part of the mind is just society's garbage bin. It is merely an accumulation of impressions that you have gathered from outside. Anybody who walks by you stuffs something into your head and moves on: your parents, teachers, friends, enemies, preachers and just everyone – you have no choice about whom to receive from or not receive from. If you say, 'I don't like this person,' you receive much more from him than anybody else! Your ability to recycle whatever kind of garbage you have in your head is what the intellect has been reduced to.

Every bit of information in your mind, all the impressions enter only through your five sense organs. Your sense organs always perceive everything only by comparison. Where there is a comparison, there is always duality. So the sense organs are constantly establishing the duality of life. They can perceive only one part of anything; they can never comprehend the whole. Suppose I was to show you my hand: now if you see one side of my hand, you would be unable to see the other side of it; if I show you the other side of it, you wouldn't be able to perceive this side of it. Your perception is all in bits and pieces and can only give you an illusion of the whole.

Since all the accumulated information in your mind is in bits and pieces, when you keep your intellect dipped in this accumulative part of the mind, your intellect draws very wrong conclusions about life. The more people become engrossed in thought, the more joyless they may become. It is unfortunate.

Thought is not the issue, but being identified with it is the issue. People who think with clarity should be joyful. For many people, the more they think, the more incapable they become of laughing; they have enslaved their instrument of discernment to the limitations of sense perception.

If you constantly wipe

> If you constantly wipe your intellect with awareness, it becomes razor-sharp. It can cut through what is true and untrue and deliver you to a different dimension of life altogether.

your intellect with awareness, it becomes razor-sharp. It can cut through what is true and untrue and deliver you to a different dimension of life altogether. If one has to grow, if one has to reach one's ultimate nature through the process of the mind, one needs to make one's intellect *truly* discriminatory in the ultimate sense. Not in terms of dividing everything as good and bad, right and wrong, but in discerning what is real and what is illusory, what is existential and what is psychological.

The Next Step

If you consciously walk a tightrope, you have no choice but to be aware. If your intellect is constantly choosing between good and bad, it has become a prejudiced intellect. And when it is busy slotting the world into good and bad, you will most definitely fall. Don't take the tightrope literally. You could just try bringing a certain precision into the physical movements of the body. (If you do hatha yoga sadhana, it should happen anyway.) This is not about becoming self-conscious or pretentious, but about being exact. Try this with your body and see. Bring precision into every movement, every gesture. This is one way of dipping your intellect in awareness.

Awareness Is Aliveness

'Awareness is not something that you do. Awareness is aliveness. Awareness is what you are.'

What is awareness anyhow? The word means different things to different people. When we say 'awareness', do not mistake it for mental alertness. Mental alertness will only enhance your ability to survive in the world. It is doglike alertness. Awareness is not something that you do. There is a difference between a state and an action. Awareness is what you are. Awareness is aliveness.

Sleep, wakefulness, death – these are all just different levels of awareness. Suppose you were dozing and somebody gave you a little elbow treatment. *Poof!* The whole world comes back! That is not a small thing. You recreated the whole of existence instantly, isn't it? The world which was obliterated in your experience pops back. Not in seven days; in just a moment.

How do you know whether existence is there or not? Only by your experience; there is no other proof. Awareness is that which can either create or obliterate this existence. If it is not there, the whole existence disappears. That is the magic of awareness. You can take your awareness to different notches. As it goes up further and further, whole new dimensions of existence could open up in your experience. Worlds that nobody had imagined in their wildest possible dreams become a living reality for you.

Suppose you were to ask a sleeping person without waking him up, 'Does the world exist?' his answer would be no. The world does not exist as far as he is concerned because he is not aware. But even in sleep you are not completely unaware. The difference between a sleeping man and dead man is one of awareness.

Similarly, between a wakeful man and an awakened man, also, there is a difference. An awakened man sleeps too, but he has managed to achieve so much awareness that some part of him does not sleep. For him also the body rests, but some part of him remains *on* all the time. This is because he has notched up his awareness to another level.

Awareness is a process of inclusiveness, a way of embracing this entire existence. You cannot *do* it, but you can set the right conditions so that it happens. Don't try to *be* aware. It will not work. If

> Awareness is a process of inclusiveness, a way of embracing this entire existence.

you keep your body, mind and energies properly aligned and cultivated, awareness will blossom. You will become far more alive than you are right now.

THE NEXT STEP

You can try this experiment today. When you move from wakefulness to sleep – at that moment, make an attempt to be aware. This practice can be done in bed, following the instructions in the DVD enclosed with this book. If you can be aware at the last moment, you will be aware throughout your sleep. If you are aware at the moment of death, you will be aware beyond also. Start practising with sleep. Sleep is nothing but temporary death. Each day you have the possibility of becoming aware of this dimension.

Wishing Tree

'If you generate a powerful thought and let it out, it will always manifest itself.'

Your mind can be in five different states.

It could be inert – that means it is not activated at all; it is in a rudimentary state. If you energize it, it becomes active but scattered. If you energize it further, it is no longer scattered, but oscillating. If you energize it further, it becomes one-pointed. If you energize it still further, it will become conscious. If your mind is conscious, it is magic; it is a miracle; it is the bridge to the beyond.

Inert minds are not a problem. Someone who is very simple-minded and whose intellect is still not effervescent has no trouble. He eats well, and he sleeps well. It is only people who can think who cannot sleep! Simple-minded people perform all the activities of the body far better than so-called intellectual people. There is a certain peace in them because you need some intelligence to create disturbance and chaos. An inert human mind is closer to animal nature than human nature.

The moment you pump in energy, the mind becomes active. But it could be scattered. Some people, when they begin spiritual practices, may experience a new level of effervescence. They may not be able to handle it, unless the atmosphere is conducive. This effervescence in the mind, powered by new energy levels in the system, may be understood and interpreted as disturbance by some. There is this pervasive psychosis among people, a tendency to fear everything that is new. But in reality, one is merely moving from inertness towards a higher level of aliveness.

Those whose minds were very scattered will see this improving, once they start spiritual practices. But now the mind starts oscillating – one day this way, another day that way. This is a huge improvement over being scattered, moment to moment, in ten different places.

If the mind is already an oscillating mind and you energize it further, then slowly the mind becomes one-pointed. That is far better, but most importantly the mind should become *conscious.* It is not your computer, car or spacecraft, but the human mind, which is the most miraculous thing in this existence – if only you could use it consciously. The reason why for one person success comes so easily and naturally, while for another it is a struggle, is because one person thinks the way he wants to, and another thinks against himself.

A well-established or well-organized human mind is referred to as a *kalpavriksha,* or a wishing tree that grants any boon.

In this mind, whatever you ask for becomes a reality. All you need to do is to develop the mind to a point where it becomes a kalpavriksha, not a source of madness.

Once your thought gets organized, your emotions will also get organized. Once your thoughts and emotions are organized, your energies in turn get organized in the same direction. Once these are organized, your very body will get organized. Once all these are organized in one direction, your ability to create and manifest what you want is phenomenal.

> If your mind is conscious, it is magic; it is a miracle; it is the bridge to the beyond.

Today modern science is proving that the whole existence is just a reverberation of energy, a vibration. Similarly, your thought is also a vibration. If you generate a powerful thought and let it out, it will always manifest itself. For this to happen, it is important that you do not impede and weaken your thought by creating a negative thought process.

Generally, people use faith as a means to remove negative thoughts. Once you become a thinking human being, your faith is rarely very deep. It does not matter how much faith you think you have, somewhere doubts always crop up. The way your minds are made, this moment if God appears right here, you will not surrender to Him; you will want an investigation to find out whether He is really God or not. With this kind of mind, don't waste your time on faith.

There is an alternative, which is commitment. If you simply commit yourself to creating what you really care for, now once again your thought gets organized in such a way that there are no hurdles. Your thought flows freely towards what you want, and once this happens, its manifestation will naturally follow.

THE NEXT STEP

To create what you really care for, the first and foremost thing is that what you want must be well manifested in your mind. Is that what you really want? Do this carefully. How many times in your life you have thought 'This is it.' The moment you get there you realized that was not it at all! So we must first explore what we really want. Once that is clear there is a continuous process of thought in that direction. When you maintain a steady stream of thought, without changing direction, it will manifest as a reality in your life. That's a guarantee.

The Grime of Identity

'Your information about anything which is not a living experience for you is pure garbage. Maybe very holy garbage, but it does not liberate you; it only entangles you.'

The process of discrimination happens because of the intellect. The intellect is like a scalpel which cuts through everything to give you some sense of perception. If a scalpel or knife has to proceed effortlessly, it is extremely important that whatever it cuts through does not stick to it.

Suppose you use a knife to cut a cake today; tomorrow you cut bread with it; the day after tomorrow you cut something else. If the residues from all these stick to this knife, after some time it becomes a useless instrument. You must have experienced this: you cut an onion, and after that mangoes or apples; everything tastes like onion. That knife becomes more of a nuisance than a help! Or in other words, once your intellect gets identified with something, it gets chained by this, and so you have a completely distorted experience of reality.

Let me tell you a story. Akbar, the emperor, lost his mother when he was a baby. So another woman, who had a son of her own, was brought in to nurse Akbar. This woman breastfed Akbar and later on she was rewarded for this. Her child, slightly older than Akbar, was allotted a few villages and made a small king. Many years later, Akbar became a prominent emperor but this boy, who didn't have the necessary intelligence or capability, squandered everything. He lost all his property.

When he was about thirty-two years old, this man got an idea. 'My mother nursed the emperor, and in some way because we drank the same mother's milk, we are brothers. So, I should also be an emperor. I am an elder brother. I should be the real emperor because I am older than Akbar.'

With this idea in his head, he went to Akbar and told him, 'See, my mother nursed you, we have drunk milk from the same breast. We're brothers, and I'm elder to you. Now, I'm poor, you're an emperor; how can you leave me like this?'

Akbar was deeply moved. He welcomed him, set him up in the palace, and treated him like a king. Since he grew up in a village, the man was not accustomed to the ways of the palace and did many stupid things, but Akbar kept saying, 'He's my elder brother.' He introduced him to everybody as his elder brother.

This went on for some time. Then it was time for the man to leave. He had to go back to his village for something. Then Akbar said, 'Okay, you lost those villages. I'll give you five new villages for you to rule. A small kingdom of your own.'

Then the man said, 'I see that you have become this successful because there are lots of smart people around you. I don't have anybody like that, that's why I'm lost. If only I had good advisers and ministers, I would have also built a major empire like you. And above all, you have Birbal. He's so smart. If I only had somebody like him I would also become a great emperor.'

So Akbar said, 'If you wish, you may take Birbal with you.'

The man was thrilled. 'Yes, if I have Birbal, I will also become a great emperor.'

Akbar ordered Birbal, 'You must go with my elder brother.'

Birbal said, 'Your Highness, your elder brother deserves someone better. I also have an elder brother. I could send him instead.'

Akbar thought that was a great idea because he really didn't want to lose Birbal. But he was identified with this man as an elder brother. Relieved, he said, 'That's a great idea.'

The next day, when this man was going to leave, a big farewell was planned in court. Everybody was assembled, and waiting for Birbal to bring his elder brother.

Birbal entered with a bull in tow.

Akbar asked, 'What is *this*?'

Birbal said, 'This is my elder brother. Both of us drank milk from the same mother.'

Once your intellect gets identified with something, you function within the ambit of this identity. Your mind, which should have been a ladder to the divine, is either stumbling through the mediocre or has become a straight stairway to hell.

Whatever you are identified with, all your thought and

emotion springs from that identity. Right now suppose you identify yourself as a man, all your thought and emotion flow from that identity. Or if you identify yourself with your nationality, or religion, they will flow from those identities. Whatever thoughts and emotions you have, these represent a certain level of prejudice; your mind is itself a certain kind of prejudice.

Once you are identified with something that you are not, the mind is an express train you cannot stop. If you put the mind on full steam and want to apply the brakes – it does not work. You must take your foot off the throttle first before you brake. Dis-identify with everything that you are not, and you will see, the mind will be just blank and empty. If you want to use it, you can; otherwise it will be simply empty. That is how it should be.

Whatever you identify yourself with, when death confronts you, it all drops. If you have any sense, you will learn now; if you don't learn now, death will teach you. Have no doubts about that.

If a human being does not look at himself as a man or a woman, if he does not encumber his intellect with any identifications—of body, family, qualifications, society, caste, creed, community, nation, even the species, and the million other identities that one takes on in life – he will naturally proceed to his ultimate nature.

If you employ your intelligence and make an attempt to reach your ultimate nature, this is called gnana yoga. Gnana yoga is pure intellect. Gnana yogis cannot afford to believe or identify themselves with anything; if they do, their intellect is finished. But what has happened to gnana yoga in India is that its proponents believe in so many things: 'I am Atman, I am Paramatman,' etc. They believe in the arrangement

> Very few people have the necessary intellect to pursue gnana yoga hundred per cent.

of the cosmos, the shape and size of the soul. They have read all these things in a book. This is not gnana yoga. Your information about anything which is not a living experience for you is pure garbage. Maybe very holy garbage, but it does not liberate you; it only entangles you.

On a certain day, a bull was grazing in a field. *Chomp, chomp, chomp.* He went deep into the forest, and after weeks of grazing on lush grass, became nice and fat. A lion, who was past his prime and having difficulty hunting wild creatures, saw this nice fat bull, pounced upon him, killed him and ate him up. His stomach became full. With great satisfaction, he roared. A few hunters were passing by. They heard the roar, tracked him down and shot him dead.

Moral of the story: when you are so full of bull, you should not open your mouth.

All the time, people seem to be opening their mouths about just about anything. Right now, scholarship is often just an accumulation of information whose antecedents are questionable. Such pursuits are only of social relevance, and have no existential relevance whatsoever.

Very few people have the necessary intellect to pursue gnana yoga hundred per cent. Most would need a huge amount of preparation. There is a whole system to make your intellect so razor-sharp that it does not stick to anything. It is very time-consuming because the mind is tricky; it will create a million illusions. Gnana yoga as a part of your pursuit is okay; as a sole pursuit, it is for a very rare few.

THE NEXT STEP

Just sit alone for a day, if possible – or at least for an hour. No reading, no television, nothing. Just see in the course of this hour or day what thoughts dominate your mind -- whether it is food, sex, your car, your furniture, your jewellery, whatever. If you find yourself thinking recurrently about people or things, your identification is essentially with your body. If your thoughts are about what you would like to do in the world, your identification is essentially with your mind. Everything else is a complex branch-out of these two aspects. (This is not a value judgement. This is just a way of knowing what stage of life you're at. How quickly you want to evolve depends on your own choices.)

Moral Prejudice

'If you seek an element of spirituality, the first and foremost step is that you drop your ideas of good and bad.'

One of the biggest problems is that right from your childhood morality is imposed on you. People have taught you what is right and wrong, good and bad. These are very strong points of identity. Whatever you consider good, you naturally get identified with. Whatever you consider bad, you are naturally repelled by it. This attraction to one thing and aversion to another is the basis of identification. The nature of your mind is that whatever you are averse to, dominates it. Suppose somebody told you, 'This is good; that is evil. Do not think about the evil.' Now, if you resist, that supposedly 'evil' thought becomes a full-time job; there is nothing else going on in your head!

For somebody who thinks he is very good, nobody in the

world is okay. Anyway, where did you get the idea that you are good? Only by comparison, isn't it? So you are only good in relation to the bad. People who think they are good are invariably overbearing and hard to live with. The idea of moral superiority has been the source of too many inhuman acts in the world to be ignored.

'Good' people usually know all the 'bad' things; they are just managing to avoid them! If you are avoiding something, it probably means you are constantly thinking about it. Avoiding something is not freedom from it. It means your goodness comes from exclusion: 'He is not okay, she is not okay.' Real purity, on the other hand, comes from inclusion.

> Your ideas of goodness are just a certain level of prejudice against life.

These ideas of good and bad, right and wrong are all your mental nonsense; they have nothing to do with life as such. What was considered to be very good a hundred years ago is intolerable today. What you think is very good, your children hate. Your ideas of goodness are just a certain level of prejudice against life.

On a certain day, two Irishmen were working on the street, in front of a London brothel. They saw a Protestant minister coming their way. He rolled up his collar, put his head down and quietly slipped into the brothel. They looked at each other and said, 'See, what else can you expect from a Protestant? Not much difference between a Protestant and a prostitute anyway.'

Then they continued to work. After some time a Jewish rabbi

came. He had a muffler around his throat, almost covering his face. He ducked into the brothel too. Then they felt distressed. 'What has happened? Times have gone bad. A religious man in a brothel! Why is this happening?' They were pained by this.

Then after a while the local bishop came, and he looked this way and that, tightened his cloak around himself and slipped into the brothel.

One of the men turned to the other and said, 'One of the girls must be really sick.'

The moment you get chained to your ideas of goodness you are completely twisted out! Your intellect is functioning around these identifications in such a way that you never see anything the way it is. If you seek an element of spirituality, the first and foremost thing is that you drop your ideas of good and bad. You learn to look at life just the way it is.

People often ask: don't we need morality in our lives? The fact is, the essential nature of humanity has been suppressed and distorted in so many ways that the substitute of 'morality' has been brought in to bring some order and sanity to our lives. If our humanity were alive, there would be no need for morality at all.

Morality differs from person to person, according to times, places, situations -- and convenience. But wherever humanity finds its expression, at any time in history or in any place, it has always been the same. On the surface, in our values, morals and ethics, each one of us may be different. But if you know how to pierce a person deep enough to touch this humanity, each one of us will do things the same way. To impose morality, you don't need any involvement with people; you just have to be instructed; it can even be written on stone for you! But if you want to bring forth humanity in a person, it takes much more involvement; you have to give yourself.

Morality is worthwhile because it brings social order, but it causes inner havoc. Humanity will also bring social order but without any enforcement; it makes the human being beautiful. Only if you allow your humanity to overflow within you, will divinity naturally flower. Morality never brought divinity; instead, it has brought you guilt, shame and fear, because nobody can fulfil the kind of morals which have been set down by religion.

Make a list of all the things that the major religions of the world call a 'sin', and you will find that just to be alive is a sin. If you are born it is a sin; if you menstruate it is a sin; if you copulate it is a sin. Forget about all this, even if you as much as eat a chocolate, you could commit a sin. Everything is a sin. Since the very process of life is a sin, you are always in a state of guilt or terror. If people did not have so much fear and guilt in them, the temples, mosques and churches in the world wouldn't be full. If you were joyful by yourself, you would go and sit on the beach, or listen to the whisper of the leaves in the tree. Only because these religions have instilled such a sense of guilt, fear and shame about everything, you are ashamed of your very existence, of your very biology. Now you have to go to the temple, mosque or church to wash it off.

People will always find ways to subvert values, morals and ethics. But when you are joyful, when you are pleasant within yourself, you are naturally nice to everyone around you. Spirituality does not mean going away from life; it means becoming alive to the core, in the fullest possible way. This is why my whole work is simply to make human beings truly blissful. With age, physical agility may go down, but the level of joy and aliveness need not. If your level of joy and aliveness is declining, you are simply committing suicide in instalments.

Unfortunately, all kinds of belief systems are passing off as spirituality. The spiritual process is always a quest, a seeking. There is a significant difference, because believing means you have assumed something which

> Make a list of all the things that the major religions of the world call a 'sin', and you will find that just to be alive is a sin.

you do not know; seeking means you have realized that you do not know, which brings an enormous amount of flexibility. The moment you believe something, you are bringing a certain rigidity into the very life process that you are. This rigidity is not just in attitude; it percolates into every aspect of your life and is also the cause of an enormous amount of suffering in the world. Human society is always a reflection of its people. Creating human beings who are flexible and willing to look at everything rather than being stuck in their ideas and opinions makes for a different kind of society.

Yoga is a method that has worked wonderfully for me, and for millions of people. It is a method, an instrument, a scientific process. It does not take faith or belief or optimism; we know it works because of proven results. It is just like if you have a good seed, if you create the right atmosphere, it will sprout. Creating the right atmosphere is the only work. You do not have to make anything else happen; no teaching of great morals or of love is needed. If your humanity is in full swing, you do not need morality; you are a beautiful human being anyway.

Being a full-fledged human includes all the possibilities of life. Let your striving be towards how to liberate this life rather than how to control it. Striving for liberation is an insurance against all negative activity, because all negativity springs from an individual's limitations. From limitations to liberation, that is the way.

Limits of Logic

'Moments of extreme logic are moments of suicide.'

Without logical thinking, there is no survival on this planet. But at the same time, if you think too logically, you will not survive.

Let us say you wake up tomorrow morning and start thinking one hundred per cent logically. Do not think about the sunrise, the birds in the sky, your child's face, the flowers blooming in your garden. Just think logically. Now, you actually have to get up. Then you have to go to the toilet, brush your teeth, eat, work, eat, work, eat, sleep. Again, tomorrow morning, you do the same thing. For the next thirty, forty, fifty or sixty years, you have to do the same thing. If you think one hundred per cent logically, there is no reason for you to be alive!

One day in New York City, a man was walking home. He was late from the office, and he suddenly had a romantic idea.

He went to the florist, bought a huge bunch of red roses, went home and knocked on the door. His wife opened the door.

She just looked at him and started screaming. 'Today has been a terrible day. The faucet has been leaking, the basement is flooded, the children had a food fight, and I had to clean the whole place, the dog has been sick, my mother is not well, and you have the guts to come home *drunk*!'

Moments of extreme logic are moments of suicide. So if you think one hundred per cent logically, there is really no possibility of life. Only if you know to what extent your logic should go (and where it should not go) will you know the beauty of life.

Thinking Yourself Out of Life

'Have you come here to experience life or to think about life?'

Someone told you, 'I think therefore I am.' Is that really true? It is only because you exist that you can generate a thought, isn't it? Your thought process has become so compulsive, and your focus has shifted from your existence to your thought to such an extent, that now you are beginning to believe that you exist because you think. Even without your silly thoughts, existence *is*. What can you think, really? Just the nonsense that you have gathered and recycled. Can you think something other than what has been fed into your head? All you are doing is recycling old data. This recycling has become so important that you even dare to say 'I think, therefore I am.' And that has become the world's way of life.

Because you are, you can think. If you choose, you can fully be and still not think. The most beautiful moments in your life – moments of bliss, moments of joy, moments of ecstasy, moments of utter peace – were moments when you were not thinking about anything. You were just living.

Do you want to be a living being or a thinking being? Right now, ninety per cent of the time you are only thinking about life, not living life. Have you come here to experience life or to think about life? Everybody can think up their own nonsense whichever way they want; it need not have anything to do with reality. Your psychological process is a very small happening compared to the life process, but right now it has become far more important. We need to shift the significance to the life process once again.

Aristotle is known as the father of modern logic; his logic was immaculate. He was intellectually brilliant, no question about that, but he tried to stretch logic to all aspects of life, and in many ways he was crippled.

There is a story (I do not know if it is a fact, but it smells true). One day, Aristotle was walking on the beach. A glorious sunset was happening, but he had no time for such petty daily events. He was thinking seriously about some great problem of existence, because for Aristotle, existence is a problem, and he believes he is going to solve it. Thinking seriously, he was walking up and down the beach. There was another man on the beach who was doing something very intensely – so intensely that even Aristotle could not ignore him.

You know, people who think too much about their own nonsense end up ignoring life around them. They are the people who don't smile at anybody or even look at anybody

> The most beautiful
> moments in your life
> are those moments
> when you were
> not thinking about
> anything.

in the world. They have no eyes to look at a flower, a sunset, a child or a smiling face – or if it is an unsmiling face, they have no inclination to make it smile; they have no such small duties or small cares in the world! They ignore all the life around them because they are all *busy*, solving the problems of existence.

But Aristotle could not ignore this man, and he closely observed what he was doing: this man was going to the ocean, coming back, going to the ocean, coming back, all with great intensity. So Aristotle stopped and asked, 'Hey, what are you up to?'

The man said, 'Don't disturb me, I am doing something very important,' and went on and on.

Aristotle became even more curious and asked, 'What *are* you doing?'

The man said, 'Don't disturb me, something very important.'

Aristotle said, 'What is this important thing?'

The man showed a little hole he had dug in the sand, and he said, 'I am emptying the ocean into this hole.' He had a tablespoon in his hand.

Aristotle looked at this and laughed. Now, Aristotle is the kind who can spend a year without a single moment of laughter, because he is *intellect*. It takes a heart to laugh. Intellect cannot laugh; it can only dissect.

But even Aristotle laughed at this and said, 'This is ridiculous! You must be insane. Do you know how vast this ocean is? How can you ever empty this ocean into this little hole? And that too, with a tablespoon? At least if you have a bucket, there's some chance. Please give this up; this is madness, I am telling you.'

The man looked at Aristotle, threw the spoon down and said, 'My job is already done.'

Aristotle said, 'What do you mean? Forget about the ocean being empty; even the hole is not full. How can you say your job is done?'

The other man was Heraclitus. Heraclitus stood up and said, 'I am trying to empty the ocean into this hole with a tablespoon. You are telling me it's ridiculous, it's madness, so I should give it up. What are *you* trying to do? Do you know how vast this existence is? It can contain a billion oceans like this and more, and you are trying to empty it into the small hole of your head – and with what? With tablespoons called thoughts. Please give it up. It's utterly ridiculous.'

If you want to know the experiential dimensions of life, you will never know it with petty thought. It does not matter how well you can think, human thought is still petty. Even if you have Einstein's brain working within you, it is still petty because thought cannot be bigger than life. Thought can only be logical, functioning between two polarities. If you want to know life in its immensity, you need something more than your thoughts, something more than your logic, something more than your intellect.

This is the choice you have: either you learn to live with

> If you want to know life in its immensity, you need something more than your thoughts, something more than your logic, something more than your intellect.

creation, or you create your own nonsensical creation in your head. Which option do you want to exercise? Right now, most people are living in a psychological space, not in an existential space. And so they are insecure, because it can collapse any moment.

The planet is spinning on time. Not a small event. All galaxies are going perfectly well, the whole cosmos is doing great. But you have one nasty little thought crawling through your head, and it is a bad day.

You have the freedom to think whatever you want. Why don't you just think pleasant thoughts? The problem is just this: you have a computer for which you have not bothered to find the keypad. If you had the keypad, you might type the right words, isn't it? You don't have the keypad, and you are punching your computer like a cave man, so all the wrong words keep coming up. Try this with your computer; the result will look like an obscenity.

You have lost your perspective of life because you think you are much more than you are. In cosmic space, if you look at yourself in perspective, you are less than a speck of dust, but you think *your* thought – which is less than a speck in you – should determine the nature of existence. What I think and what you think is not of any importance. What is important is the grandeur of existence—the only reality.

You have heard of the word 'Buddha.' One who has risen above his intellect, or one who has risen above the discriminatory and logical dimension of his life, is a Buddha. Human beings have invented millions of ways to suffer. For all this the manufacturing unit is just in your mind. When you have risen above your mind, this is the end of suffering. When there is no fear of suffering, there is absolute freedom. Only when this happens, a man is free to experience life beyond his limitations. So being a Buddha means that you have become a witness to your own intellect. The essence of yoga and meditation is just this: once you have a clear space between you and your mind, you experience a completely different dimension of existence.

The Next Step

You could try this simple practice. Set your tap – or any similar contraption – in such a way that only five to ten drops fall per minute. See if you can observe each drop – how it forms, how it falls, how it splashes on the ground. Do this for fifteen to twenty minutes a day. You will suddenly become conscious of so many things around and within you that you are completely unaware of right now.

Knowing without Thought

'What a horrible choice, if you have chosen a boxful of intelligence over a cosmos of intelligence.'

It does not matter what kind of engineering course you may have done, there is still something to learn from a beehive.

Have you watched a beehive closely? It is a fabulous piece of engineering! It is the best apartment complex that you could ever imagine. It is so beautifully structured, and in any kind of weather have you ever seen a beehive falling off a tree, have you? It is a fabulous piece of work, but do the bees have engineering plans in their head? No, these plans are there in their body. They know exactly what to do because of a blueprint in their system.

Spiritual knowledge was always transmitted like this – not by thought, not by words, but just in the way a bee knows how to build a hive. It is a kind of download. Once this is downloaded, everything that you need to know is there, but not in the form of thought. If you download a certain type of software onto your computer, you don't have to understand how all of it works; you press one key, it produces a result; another key, another result. You do not have to listen to every

> The most sophisticated machine, including the brain, was created by this intrinsic intelligence.

word that is written in the software; you just download it. Suddenly, you have a different kind of phenomenon.

There is an intrinsic intelligence within you which, as we have discussed earlier, is capable of transforming a piece of bread into flesh, a banana into a human being. The most sophisticated machine, including the brain, was created by this intrinsic intelligence. Right now you are just trying to use a certain part of your brain, and you think that is intelligence. No. There is something within you which can create an entire brain. That something functions in a different way altogether.

My thought is very organic because I don't think with my head but with every cell in my body. There is a certain level of 'integratedness' or homogeneity about it because I don't use just my head to think. I don't have much thought in my mind at all, unless I *want* to think.

Nothing has ever been out of place in this existence. Things have been out of place in human societies. Between this piece of life and that piece of life there is a context, there is a comparison. But for the intelligence which is making life happen, there is no context, no comparison. You cannot say whether it is now in place or not – it is *always* in place. There is no other way for it to be.

The whole effort – the sadhana, the yoga, the spiritual process – is just this: moving from this bone-box of intelligence to a cosmos of intelligence. This is the spiritual journey. What a horrible choice, if you have chosen a boxful of intelligence over a cosmos of intelligence.

THE NEXT STEP

First remove from the mind the idea that thought is intelligence. The whole process of creation, from a single atom to the cosmic, is a fantastic expression of intelligence. Right now within your own body, there is a throbbing intelligence which is the very source of creation. With all the overrated intellect that you have, can you even understand the activity of a single cell in your body in its entirety? The first step towards moving from the trap of the intellect to the lap of a larger intelligence is to recognize every aspect of life – from a grain of sand to a mountain, a drop to an ocean, the atomic to the cosmic – as a manifestation of a far greater intelligence than your minuscule intellect. If you take this one step, life will start speaking to you.

No Head, No Heart

'The way you think is the way you feel.'

People often say their head tells them one thing and their heart another. In such cases, they ask, which should they follow: head or heart?

The fact is, there is no head and heart separation; you are one whole. Let us first of all understand what is being referred to as the 'head' and the 'heart'. You are referring to the thought process as head and your feeling as the heart. I want you to look at this carefully and with utmost sincerity. You will see: the way you think is the way you feel.

If I think you are a wonderful person, I will have sweet emotions towards you. If I think you are a horrible person, I will have nasty emotions towards you. Can I think you are a wonderful person and have nasty emotions towards you? Or can I think you are a horrible person and have sweet emotions towards you? It is not possible. If you make someone your enemy and then try to love him, that is hard work. Let us not make hard work of the simple aspects of life.

The way you think is the way you feel, but thought and feeling seem to be different in your experience. Thought has a certain clarity, a certain agility about itself. Today, you think this is a very wonderful person and you have sweet emotions. Suddenly, he does something that you don't like, and now you think he is horrible. Your thought tells you he is horrible immediately, but your emotion cannot change immediately. It struggles. If it is sweet now, next moment, it cannot turn bitter. It takes time to turn around; its turning arc is wide. Depending on the strength of your emotion, maybe it will take three days or three months or three years, but after some time, it will turn around.

> Emotion is just the juicier part of the thought.

Let us not create this conflict between head and heart. The way you think *is* the way you feel. Emotion is just the juicier part of the thought. You can enjoy it, but it is always the thought which leads the emotion, whether you recognize it or not. Are your emotions steady about anyone? Emotion also chatters, goes this way and that way, but it is more sappy, and not as agile as thought. Since the turning arc is different and the intensity is hugely different, it looks like they are separate. But they are not separate; just like sugarcane and its juice aren't separate.

Thought is not as intense as emotion in most people's

experience. You usually do not think as intensely as you feel. But if you generate an intense enough thought, it can also overwhelm you. Only five to ten per cent of people may be capable of generating the kind of thought that is so intense that there is no need for emotion. Ninety per cent of people can only generate intense emotions because they have never done the necessary work in the other direction. But there are people whose thought is very deep. They don't have much emotion, but they are very deep thinkers.

What you normally think of as 'mind' is the thought process or intellect. Whether I am speaking 'from my intellect' or from 'the bottom of my heart', I would say both are just the mind. One is the logical aspect; another is the deeper emotional aspect. '*Buddhi*' means intellect. The deeper dimension of the mind you call heart, but in yoga this deeper emotional mind is known as '*manas*'. The way I feel is still the mind. The way I think is also the mind. Both are very much connected.

Do not create two different poles within yourself. Thought and feeling are not different. One is dry. Another is juicy. Enjoy both. Don't separate them.

Intoxication

'Yogis are not against pleasure. They are unwilling to settle for little pleasures, that's all.'

Shiva, the Adiyogi, they say, constantly drank *somarasa*. He just imbibed the moonbeams which he carried always in his hair and was constantly drunk.

Yogis are not against pleasure. They are unwilling to settle for little pleasures, that's all. They know if you drink a glass of wine, it just gets you a little buzzy, but tomorrow morning it gives you a headache and the works. They are not willing to settle for that. To enjoy the intoxication you must be alert, isn't it? All the time, totally drunk but fully alert -- only then you can enjoy it. The science of yoga gives this pleasure to you. The end goal is not just intoxication. This blissful state eliminates the fear of suffering.

Only when this idea – 'What will happen to me?' – is completely eliminated from your mind would you dare to explore life. Otherwise you only want to protect it. Once the fear of suffering is taken away from your life, you can plunge into any situation without hesitation. If they ask you to go to hell, you will go there because you have no fear of suffering.

When everybody was talking about going to heaven, Gautama the Buddha said, 'You say everything is fine in heaven, so what will I do there? Let me go to hell and do something, because anyway I cannot suffer.'

As long as the fear of suffering is constantly playing its role, you will not dare to explore deeper dimensions of life. Only this body needs to be protected; nothing else in you needs protection. Whatever ideas, philosophies and belief systems you are attached to, if you are willing, you can just drop them right now and recreate your whole life the very next moment.

Love Mantra

'There is really no such thing as conditional love and unconditional love: it is just that there are conditions and there is love.'

And what about love? Is there such a thing as unconditional love among human beings? These are frequently asked questions.

Generally, we have made relationships within frameworks that are comfortable and profitable for us. People have physical, psychological, emotional, financial or social needs to fulfil. To fulfil these needs, one of the best ways is to tell people, 'I love you.' This so-called 'love' has become like a mantra: open sesame. You can get what you want by saying it.

One day Shankaran Pillai went to a park. On a stone bench there sat a pretty woman. He went and settled down on the same bench. After a few minutes he moved a little closer to her. She moved away. Again he waited for a few minutes then inched a little closer to her. She moved away. He waited, then inched even closer. Then she moved to the very end of the bench. He reached out and put his hand on her. She shrugged him off. He sat there for a while, then he went down on his knees, plucked a flower, gave it to her and said, 'I love you. I love you like I have never loved anybody in my life.'

She melted. Nature took over and they had their way with each other. It was getting late in the evening; Shankaran Pillai got up and he said, 'I need to leave. It's eight o'clock. My wife will be waiting.'

She said, 'What? You're leaving? Just now you said you loved me!'

'Yes, but it's time. I need to go.'

Every action that we do is in some way to fulfil certain needs. If you see this, there is a possibility that you can grow into love as your natural quality. But you can go on fooling yourself into believing that the relationships you have made for convenience, comfort and well being are actually relationships of love. I am not saying there is no experience of love at all in those relationships, but it is within certain limitations. It does not matter how much 'I love you' has been said; if a few expectations and requisites are not fulfilled, things will fall apart. Love is a quality; it is not something to do with somebody else.

> Love is a quality; it is not something to do with somebody else.

There is really no such thing as conditional love and unconditional love: it is just that there are conditions and there is love. When you talk about love, it has to be unconditional. The moment there is a condition, it just amounts to a transaction. Maybe a convenient transaction, maybe a good arrangement – maybe many of you made excellent arrangements in life – but that will not fulfil you; that will not transport you to another dimension. It is just convenient. When you say 'love', it need not necessarily be convenient; most of the time it is not. It takes life.

Love is not a great thing to do, because it eats you up. If you have to be in love, you should not *be*. The English expression 'falling in love' is very significant. You don't climb in love, you don't walk in love, you don't stand in love, you *fall* in love. You as a person must be willing to fall, only then it can happen. If your personality is kept strong in the process, it is just a convenient situation, that's all. We need to recognize what is a transaction and what is truly a love affair. A love affair need not be with any particular person; you could be having a great love affair, not with anybody in particular, but with life.

What you do, what you do not do, is according to the circumstances around you. Our actions are as the external situation demands. What you do outside is always subject

> You could be having a great love affair, not with anybody in particular, but with life.

to many conditions. But love is an inner state – how you are within yourself can definitely be unconditional.

THE NEXT STEP

Love is never between two people. It is what happens within you, and what happens within you need not be enslaved to someone else. For fifteen to twenty minutes daily, go sit with something that means nothing to you – maybe a tree, or a pebble, or a worm or an insect. After some time, you will find you can look upon it with as much love as you do your wife or husband or your mother or your child. Maybe the worm does not know this. That doesn't matter. If you can look at everything lovingly, the whole world becomes beautiful in your experience. You realize love is not something that you do; love is the way you are.

Devotion: A Dimensional Shift

'In devotion, there is no shred of sanity; there is no way to recover.'

The most generous thing that you can do in life is to live to your peak and to set an example to the rest of the world that there is a way to live beyond all limitations. Sparing life for tomorrow is not generosity. It simply means you are so stingy that you cannot love totally, laugh totally, or be joyful totally. You are a *kanjoos* – a miser – on all levels!

Devotion means you are not a kanjoos – you are full of juice! Everything in you is flowing out all the time. A devotee is seeing how to expend his life as rapidly, as fully as possible, not somebody who is trying to conserve life, not somebody who is planning to live tomorrow. A devotee is somebody who is living now, absolutely.

Devotion is not a love affair; it is a crazy thing. Love itself is a crazy thing, but there are shreds of sanity attached to it; you can still recover. In devotion, there is no shred of sanity; there is no way to recover.

A devotee has the sweetest experience of life. Everybody may think he is an idiot, but he is having the best time on the planet. You decide who the idiot is.

When I say 'devotion', I am not talking about belief systems. Belief is just like morality. People who believe some nonsense think they are superior to others. All that happens the moment you believe something is that your stupidity gets confident. Confidence and stupidity are a very dangerous combination, but generally you find them together. If you start looking at all the dimensions around you, you would clearly understand that what you know is so minuscule that there is no way to act with confidence. A belief system takes away this problem; it gives you enormous confidence, but it does not cure your stupidity.

Devotion is not an act; it is not directed towards something or the other; the object of devotion is immaterial. It is just that with devotion you have dissolved all the resistance in you so that the divine can transpire like breath. The divine is not an entity sitting up there; it is a living force in every moment of your life.

At a Catholic family dinner, the man came to the table, looked at the food and, as usual, he grumbled and cursed his wife and everything around him. After the cursing was over and everyone settled down, he sat down and uttered his prayer, 'Dear God, thank you for the daily bread and all the wonderful things on the table.'

There was a five-year-old girl who was meekly sitting there. You know, these five-year-old boys and girls – always extra pillows and little cushions kept for them, but still they can never really reach the plate. So, this little five-year-old girl squeaked, with the table up to her neck, 'Daddy, does God always hear all our prayers?'

> The divine is not an entity sitting up there; it is a living force in every moment of your life.

Immediately, the Christian in him became active and he said, 'Yes, of course. Every prayer we utter, He always listens to it.'

Then the girl sank a little low, because she sank into thought; the table went up over her head. After a while, she came up and said, 'But Daddy, does he also listen to all the other things that we say?'

'Yes, every moment of our life God is listening and seeing everything that we say and do.'

Then again she sank down. Again she came up and said, 'Daddy, then which does he believe?'

Tell me, which should God believe – your prayers or your curses? He is thoroughly confused! He has given up. Because we systematize or institutionalize the most loving and tender parts of life, suddenly everything loses its vibrancy, becomes lifeless. The words are there in everybody's mouths, but they do not mean anything. When we are saying something which does not really burn within us, it amounts to lying; it is better to shut up.

We are always trying to do what somebody did a thousand

years ago. Yes, when someone else did it two thousand years ago it worked for him – because of the fire in his heart. It worked because of the truth that was burning within him, not because of the words he uttered.

Devotion is not a cool thing; it's hot. That's because Truth is something that burns.

The Naked Seeress

'Devotees don't belong to this world; they just have one foot in this world.'

Over 600 years ago in southern India, there lived a woman mystic called Akka Mahadevi. Akka was a devotee of Shiva. Already in her childhood, she regarded Shiva as her husband. It was not just a belief; it was a reality for her.

The king saw her one day, and she was so beautiful that he said, 'I want this girl.' She refused. But then the king threatened that if the girl was not married to him, he would kill her parents.

She married the man, but she kept him at a physical distance. He tried to woo her, but she went on saying, 'Mahadeva is my husband.' Time passed and the king's patience wore thin. He got mad, and he tried to lay his hands upon her. She refused. 'I have another husband. His name is Shiva. He visits me, and I am with him. I can't be with you.' She was to be prosecuted because she claimed to have another husband.

When she was brought to the court, Akka said, 'Being a queen doesn't mean a thing to me. I will leave.'

Then the king saw the ease with which she was walking away, and said, 'Everything that you wear, the jewels, the clothes – everything is mine. Leave it all here and go.'

So, in the full assembly of the court, Akka just dropped all her clothes, all her possessions, and she just walked away naked. From that day she refused to wear clothes even though many people tried to convince her otherwise, because it would bring trouble to her. It was unbelievable for a woman to be walking naked on the streets of India at that time – and this was a young beautiful woman. She died very young, and within this short span she wrote some incredible poetry.

Her devotion was such that every day she begged, 'Shiva, let no food come my way. Let my body also express the longing and anguish that I am going through to become part of you. If I eat, my body will be satisfied, and my body will not know what I'm feeling. So let no food come towards me. If food does come into my hands, before I put it into my mouth, let it fall down in the mud. If it falls in the mud, before the fool that I am picks it up, let a dog come and take it away.' This was the daily prayer.

Devotees of this kind don't belong to this world; they just have one foot in this world. The power and grandeur with which they lived their lives, make them figures of lasting inspiration for humanity.

Head–Heart Cocktail

'If you want to meet Shiva, you either learn to meet him on his terms or you dissolve yourself… bhakti means you make yourself a zero; gnana means you meet him on his terms.'

Bhakti, or devotion, means to have a feeling of love for everything that you see and do not see. It means to drop the duality of like and dislike. It means 'okay' and 'not okay' do not exist for you any more; everything is okay. When some people said 'everything is God', in the past, it simply meant that that they had dropped this duality of attachment and aversion entirely.

The moment you choose something, you separate. Bhakti means becoming totally choiceless. When there is absolute choicelessness, when there is simply '*being here*', when everything envelops you or you envelop everything, then that is bhakti. This is how Truth is—all-inclusive.

In the yogic culture there are two aspects of Shiva we focus on. On one level, the word 'Shiva' literally means 'that which is not'. Everything that *is* has come from 'that which is not'. If you look up at the sky you will see many celestial objects, stars and galaxies, but still the biggest presence out there is a vast emptiness. This vast emptiness, the nothingness, is referred to as 'Shiva', and that is why he is seen as the very basis of creation. It is in the lap of this nothingness that the whole creation is happening right now.

Another dimension of Shiva in the yogic culture is that of the Adiyogi, the first yogi. The yogic culture seamlessly moves from Shiva being the basis of everything, to Shiva being the first yogi. Because this is a dialectical culture, we do not distinguish between the ultimate nature and the one who has experienced the ultimate nature.

So if you want to meet Shiva, you must either learn to meet him on his terms or dissolve yourself. If you have to be with a king, either you also have

[Bhakti means becoming totally choiceless.]

to be a king or you must be his humblest servant. These are the two ways. Gnana and bhakti mean this: bhakti means you make yourself a zero; gnana means you meet him on his terms. Otherwise, there is no meeting.

People on the path of gnana are very straight. People on the path of bhakti are drunkards. Right from the ancient times bhakti has always been the most important path, because it seems to be so easily attainable. Yes, it is the quickest path, but it has many pitfalls, many traps.

The path of gnana is harder, but it is an 'eyes-open' path; bhakti is an 'eyes-closed' path. With gnana, every step that you take, forward or backward, you know where you are going. You know where you have fallen, where you stand. With bhakti, even if you have fallen in a pit, you don't know. Even if you are trapped in your own illusions, you don't know.

With emotion, there comes a tremendous intensity. Generally, for most people, emotion is always more intense than thought. That is why bhakti has been glorified and talked about more than any other path, because most people are strong in their emotions – stronger than they are in their thought or in their work.

But emotion has its limitations. Without gnana, without a proper understanding, without opening up the seat of your wisdom, just walking this path of emotion could produce hallucinatory effects. It could be very beautiful, joyous, ecstatic, but a certain stagnation could occur.

On the other hand, without bhakti, without *bhava,* or emotion, the yogic practices just become barren, dry, lifeless. Without a sense of bhakti, your gnana often becomes simply a hair-splitting exercise.

Many people believe that devotion has no place in logic. Logic is essentially a cutting tool. If you want to look at something, you can cut through it with your logic. If your logic is like a machete, if you cut something it will fall into two pieces. But if the knife of logic that you are employing is very fine, you can cut through it all, still leaving it in one piece.

The stories about swordsmanship always talk about how when a fine swordsman uses his sword and cuts a tree, the tree should not even know; it should still stand as one. If your logic becomes this refined, then you will see devotion fits perfectly into the logical realm of your mind. True gnana and true bhakti are not different at all.

THE NEXT STEP

A devotee knows things that you cannot even imagine. He can grasp things that you have to struggle with because there is not much of him within himself. When you are too full of self, there is no room for anything higher to happen.

You can do certain things so that you arrive at devotion, but you cannot practise it. One simple thing you can do is consider everything in this existence as higher than yourself. The stars are definitely higher, but try seeing the little pebble on the street as higher than yourself. (Anyway, it is more permanent, more stable than you. It can sit still forever!) If you learn to look at everything around you as higher than yourself, you will naturally become devout.

Embracing Mystery

'If your intelligence is sufficiently evolved and mature, the more you analyse, the more you realize you are further away from any conclusion.'

It is only a juvenile intelligence which analyses things and arrives at a conclusion. If your intelligence is sufficiently evolved and mature, the more you analyse, the more you realize you are further away from any conclusion.

Today, scientists have broken up water into its constituent parts. If you ask 'What is water?' they say 'Hydrogen and oxygen.' But why do hydrogen and oxygen become water? Why is it like that? Take a pebble and look at it. Why it is so?

Or if you have no interest in anything else just look at yourself, how did you become like this? 'Oh, my father, mother, and here I am.' But why does it become like this? What is the basis of this? If you go into just about any aspect and truly analyse it, the deeper and deeper you look at it, the further and further away from conclusion you will be. Life becomes more mysterious than ever before. If you simply sit here and breathe, you will know life better than with any deep analysis.

The more you delve into life, you will discover that it is an endless and unfathomable process. You cannot get it because you *are* it. When you realize experientially that every atom, every grain of sand, every pebble, every piece of life from the smallest to the biggest is unfathomable, naturally you will bow down in utmost devotion to everything.

Traditionally in India, you would bow down to anything you saw. It did not matter if it was a tree or a cow or a snake or rain or clouds – you just bowed down to it. You do that either because you are a fool, or you do that because you have looked at life in utmost depth, with utmost profundity. The difference between an idiot and an enlightened being is very thin. It is about the same thing, but worlds apart. The fool just enjoys whatever little he knows and one who has seen life in utmost depth enjoys it absolutely. The in-between people are the ones who constantly struggle and suffer.

One morning a man walked into his office and told his boss, 'Boss, I want you to know, three big companies are after me. You must give me a raise.'

His boss said, 'What! Which are the companies? Who wants you?'

He said, 'The electric company, the telephone company and the gas company!'

So, the in-between smart people – something is always

> That which knows how to bend will not break.

behind them or they are always busy chasing something. It goes on endlessly. An idiot can sit here quietly. A mystic can sit here quietly. The smart person cannot.

Being a devotee does not mean you are a walkover. That which knows how to bend will not break. That is why in the morning you do yoga so that your body does not break! That is so with everything within you.

If you learn to bow, to hold everything higher than yourself, it does not seem to be good for your self-esteem. Unfortunately, these days even so-called spiritual leaders are talking about self-esteem. 'Self' and 'esteem', both are a problem. Both are very limited entities; both are fragile; both will always be insecure. If you have no esteem, very good. If you have no self, fabulous! There is no problem at all.

When you can exist here as the very source of creation, why would you choose to live as merely a small piece of it?

THE NEXT STEP

When you experience something as far bigger than yourself, you will naturally bow down to it. If you want to become a devotee, bow down to something at least once an hour in all the waking moments of your life. It does not matter who or what. Don't choose. You see somebody, bow down. A tree, mountain, dog, cat – anything that you see, you bow down. See if it can become once a minute. When that happens, you cannot be using your hands and body to bow down; you simply do it within yourself. Once that becomes your way of being, you are a devotee.

ENERGY

…And Now, Yoga

'Your life energies constantly want to expand and become infinite; they do not know any other goal.'

Almost every human being is in a state of insufficiency. No matter who you are, or what you have achieved, you still want to be something more than what you are right now.

This is the process of desiring. Your desire is not about anything in particular; it is about expanding. With any amount of expansion it is not going to settle; it is always seeking to become unbounded. When this longing for expansion finds an unconscious expression, we call this greed, conquest, ambition. When it finds a conscious expression, we call it yoga.

That is why when Patanjali wrote the *Yoga Sutras*, he started in a strange way. The first chapter of the *Yoga Sutras* starts with the line, '…And now, Yoga.' Half a sentence. Such a great document on life starts with half a sentence.

If you still believe that if you find a new girlfriend, or if you get a raise, or if you buy a new house or a new car that everything will be okay in your life – then it is not yet time for yoga. Once you have seen all those things and you know it is not enough – now, yoga.

Yoga means you have transcended the differentiating nature of your intellect and experienced the oneness of existence. If you burst into an experience which is beyond the limitations of the physical then what is you and what is not you cannot be differentiated. Right now, you are identified with many things, but what you call 'myself' is a certain amount of energy. Today, as we have said before, modern science is proving beyond doubt that the entire existence is the same energy, manifesting itself in a million different ways. When Einstein says $E=mc^2$, he is just telling you everything is one energy. And religions have always been proclaiming that God is everywhere. Whether you say 'everything is one energy' or you say 'God is everywhere', it is the same, isn't it? So the very purpose of yoga is to help you beyond the experience of physical boundaries established by your body. For one moment if you break the limitations of your physical form and experience the unity of all that is around as yourself, then the very way you exist will be different.

Spirituality is to be in perfect alignment with life. It is not somebody's idea or philosophy. It is to fall in line with the natural longing of life to expand in an unlimited way and give it a conscious expression. Spiritual practices assist this longing on the level of your body, mind and energy.

Your life energies constantly want to expand and become infinite; they do not know any other goal. Your mind may be thinking of money, your body may be longing for food, but your life energies are always longing to break the boundaries set by your physical form, longing to become infinite, boundless. There are so many methods to recognize which way our

> Only if you go in the direction that your life energies want to go will you be in equanimity and harmony.

life energies want to go and consciously move in that direction.

Slowly, in the process of living, for whatever reason, either out of your ego or your misery, you may stop going the way life energies are moving. And so you start thinking that you are an entity by yourself.

If you go the way your body goes, you should know that it is going straight to the grave. Whatever you know as the mind is a complex mess of all the stuff that has gone into it. The objectives of the mind are all self-created; it may seem to be fine now, but it usually takes you completely away from the process of life.

So yoga means to distinctly experience the mental and physical process, not as the basis of yourself, but as that which is caused by you. If you manage these two instruments of body and mind consciously, then your experience of life is hundred per cent your making. The content of what you refer to as 'mind' and 'body' has come to you from outside. All you need to do is create a distance between you and everything that you accumulated from outside.

Once it happened. Shankaran Pillai was travelling to Madanapalli by train. When he got into the train he had a huge bundle on his head. He found a seat for himself and sat down with the bundle still on his head. The people around him looked at him. They waited for some time, hoping that he would put it down, but he did not.

Then somebody enquired, 'Why are you carrying this bundle on your head? Why don't you put it down?'

He said, 'No, no, no, it's all right.'

They waited for some more time, and then *their* necks started aching. They could not bear the sight of this man sitting in a train with a huge bundle on his head. They said, 'See, if there is something really precious in your bundle, put it down and sit on it. That is the safer thing to do.'

He said, 'No, nothing precious. Just clothes.'

'Then why are you carrying it on your head?'

'Oh, I don't want to burden the train.'

All the garbage that you have gathered in this life comes with you. You cannot get rid of it, but you can at least put it down. The only choice you have is to create some distance from it. Use it, but do not be identified with it. If you cannot maintain this distance, your whole vision of life will be clouded. Life can be tasted, imbibed and transcended only when there is a distinction between the psychological and the existential. All one's thoughts, emotions, ideas, memories and imaginations belong to the psychological realm.

The spiritual process means a return to life. Only if you go in the direction that your life energies want to go will you be in equanimity and harmony. Only in such a stable state would you dare to explore the highest levels of exuberance and venture into the deepest mysteries of life.

Manufacturer versus Mechanic

'Most people are choosing to go to the local mechanic simply because they have lost the access to the manufacturer.'

If you have any problem with your body, one thing that needs to be understood is the material and the method with which this body was made. When you know the very source of creation or the manufacturer of this body, and if you need to get a repair job done, would you like to go to the manufacturer or to the local mechanic? Most people choose to go to the local mechanic simply because they have lost the access to the manufacturer.

On a certain day when I was about twenty years of age, I was playing field hockey and broke my ankle. It started swelling up, and I limped to the side of the hockey field and sat there in extreme pain. The other boys were still continuing to play, and they were raising a lot of dust. In a haze of dust and pain, I was suffocating and gasping for breath. Suddenly the thought came to me, 'If the very source of creation is within me, why can't I fix this breath? Why can't I fix this broken bone?'

I sat there for about an hour and a quarter with my eyes closed, and when I opened my eyes, my breath was perfectly okay, and has been till today. And above all, the swelling in my leg had gone down and there seemed to be hardly any pain. I thought this could be because I was immobile and that numbness was setting in. Holding my foot with my hands, I gently moved it and to my amazement there was actually no pain. Very slowly, leaning on my hockey stick, I stood up, hesitant to put weight on the injured leg. When I did stand, my ankle held up and there was no pain. I was in a state of absolute disbelief because I clearly knew this was a fracture, given the nature of pain and the level of swelling that happened in a short time. (By then I had had enough experience with broken bones, considering the wild nature of my activity!) My very logically trained mind started fighting this, as it fought anything that was unfathomable. My mind always took anything that defied the framework of logic as an insult to itself. The final test of whether my ankle was really okay was to kick-start my Czechoslovakian motorcycle. These are not like today's multi-cylinder self-start machines; they had a mind of their own. If you kicked, they kicked back at you! But my ankle passed the test.

When I went home, incredulous and awestruck, I asked my physician father if by any chance it was possible that a broken bone could be fixed in a matter of an hour. He said that was rubbish. But after a while, he came back, probably feeling a bit silly about what he was about to say. He said that he had witnessed, in his early phase of medical practice, a villager without any formal education demonstrate that he could successfully fix a broken shoulder of a patient in a matter of a few hours with some leafy concoction that he carried with him and some unintelligible incantations. It went against everything he had been taught by his medical training.

Armed with this experience, I started some serious

experimentation with myself. It is very difficult to articulate that phase of my life. As days rolled by, I had to constantly readjust my ideas of what is logical. I always prided myself on having a well-structured logical intellect, but with all this experimentation, it had completely lost its neatness and geometry. Slowly it became an 'organism' which could absorb and assimilate just about anything. The Inner Engineering programme we conduct at Isha is just one by-product of a broken ankle.

Defining Your Destiny

**'If you have mastery over your life energies, your life and
destiny will be in your hands.'**

All creatures on the planet adapt to the situations in which
they exist, but humans can adapt the situations to their
requirements. Today, most people in the world are moulded by
the situations in which they exist because they exist in *reaction*
to them. Predictably, their questions would be, 'Why was I
placed in such a situation? Is it my bad luck? Is it my destiny?'

Whenever things do not happen the way you want them to,
there is a temptation to label this as 'destiny'. You try to console
yourself, reconcile yourself to your present condition. This is
a way of dealing with failure, illness or other misfortunes. Or
it may even be about success beyond one's competence. All
the things that we are unable to logically comprehend, we
conveniently call 'destiny'.

People keep asking me, 'Sadhguru, how much of my destiny can I control?' Your destiny is *your* creation. Even now you are creating it – unconsciously. Every thought, emotion, impulse and reaction that you generate within yourself is creating the course of your destiny. Life within you does not ignore anything; it takes everything that you do seriously.

Life is not recording selectively; it is recording everything in wakefulness and sleep. Because everything is recorded, this huge heap of information within you, without any particular direction or awareness, is creating a whole lot of confusion, and hence, many unexplained situations and consequences of life pass off as destiny.

So if the question is, 'What will happen to me?' the answer is, whatever you create will happen to you. But don't wait for it to happen to you. *Make* it happen the way you want it. Inner Engineering [a basic Isha programme of self-empowerment and growth] is a set of tools subtler than your physical body, intellect and emotion, designed to create your inner and outer worlds the way you want.

Many of those things that people considered to be destiny a hundred years ago, you have taken into your hands today. We have managed the disastrous destinies of diseases, infections, epidemics and famines that people experienced just a century ago. Many who were affected definitely thought it was a matter of fate, but have we not taken charge of many of these seemingly inevitable calamities? Today, what we call 'technology' is just this: within the laws of nature, everything external that can be taken charge of, we take charge of.

I was once at an international conference on how to alleviate poverty on the planet. Lots of 'responsible' people were participating, including several Nobel laureates. At one point, a participant said, 'Why are we trying to solve these problems? Isn't all this divine will?'

I said, 'Yes, if somebody else is hungry or dying, it must be the divine plan. But if *your* stomach is hungry, if *your* child is dying, you'll have your own plan, isn't it?'

Wherever we have to do something about *our* lives, we have taken it into our hands. Wherever we do not want to take it into our hands, we talk about divine will or destiny. Yoga is a science that allows you take the very process of life and death into your hands. Right now you are making the choices in your life unconsciously. That is what karma means: you are creating your destiny in total chaos, in total unawareness. Whatever you are doing unconsciously, if you start doing it consciously, that makes a world of difference. It is the difference between ignorance and enlightenment.

Taking destiny into your hands does not mean everything will happen your way. The outside world will never happen 100 per cent your way because there are too many other variables involved. Wanting the outside world to happen your way is about conquest, tyranny, dictatorship. Creating destiny does not mean you have to control every situation in this world. It simply means making yourself in such a way that whatever the nature of events and situations around you, you learn to ride those situations, not get crushed by them. Essentially, it is about steadily moving towards fulfilling your ultimate nature, no matter what the content of life is around you.

'What about the stars, the planets? Don't they decide our

destinies?' If your destiny is
decided by the planets and
stars, it means you cannot
even commit suicide! You
can neither live nor die the
way you want. (It is true
that no one has the right
to commit suicide. This
is not because of moral

> What you call
> 'destiny' is just
> something that you
> created unconsciously
> for yourself.

reasons, but because you have no right to destroy that which
you cannot recreate.) You cannot decide anything about your
life either positively or negatively because you are looking
at everything through your horoscope – which is for sure, a
horror-scope!

Should inanimate objects decide the course and the destiny
of human nature or should it be the other way round? If you
are well established in yourself, every planet can go wherever it
wants, but you will still go in the direction you want. If people
were less concerned about other planets and a little more
concerned about the well being of this one – Mother Earth – at
least we would live a little better!

So what you call 'destiny' is just something that you created
unconsciously for yourself. Karma is the process; destiny is the
result. 'Karma' literally means 'action'. Action is of many kinds:
physical, mental/emotional and energy action. If these actions
find outward expression, that is karma. The most significant
aspect of yoga is always to perform action on the level of energy,
because energy is the most unconscious part of your karma.
Beyond body, mind/emotion and energy, if action turns inward,

that is kriya. Karma is the process of binding you. Kriya is the process of liberating you.

If you do anything with your body, intellect or emotions, the resultant impressions stay with you. When you gather a huge volume of impressions, slowly these form their own tendencies, and you become like an automatic toy. These tendencies have been traditionally described as *vasana*s. The word '*vasana*' literally means 'smell'. Depending upon what type of garbage is in the bin today, that is the kind of smell that emanates from it. Depending upon what type of smell you emit, you attract certain kinds of life situations towards yourself.

Suppose today there is rotten fish in the garbage bin. It may stink for you, but so many other creatures are drawn to it. Tomorrow, if there are flowers in the garbage bin, it smells different and different kinds of creatures are drawn to it.

When I came to Coimbatore in 1987, I stayed as a guest in a local doctor's house. He was a gregarious man and was telling me of an incident that happened in his family. They were from Kerala, and his elder daughter especially loved fish. She was studying in Dehradun where she did not get fish to eat, so whenever she came home for vacation, she wanted to have it every day. His wife was a vegetarian, but she would cook fish even though she did not eat it.

There is a particular small dried fish which you may know about if you are from that part of the country. It has an incredible odour. If they are carrying it in a truck, you would like to drive two miles behind the truck or hold your breath and pass it. When it is cooked in the house, usually it is a pretty good strategy to evict your neighbours from their home! This girl wanted *that* particular fish dish to be prepared.

So as they were frying this dried fish, it was like the house was being exhumed – even the dead would rise with such an odour. The mother went into the kitchen to tell the cooks how to prepare it, but the moment the smell began to be emitted, she ran out of the kitchen because she could not stand it. Meanwhile, the girl was in the bedroom, and the moment she smelled it, she ran towards the kitchen. Both of them crashed into each other – and the mother broke her nose!

I mention this because these vasanas or tendencies are generated by a vast accumulation of impressions caused by your physical, mental and emotional actions. Your personality is just one expression of these tendencies.

Now, today if you are doing something in a particular way and someone asks you why you can't do it differently, you declare, 'This is my nature. Can't I do what I want?' This is *not* your nature. You are *not* doing

> A spiritual process means we have made up our minds to rewrite our software, consciously.

what you want. These tendencies have become compulsive within you. This is your bondage, a kind of software you are writing for yourself unconsciously. Once your software is fixed, it looks like there is only one path you can walk in your life; it looks like destiny. A spiritual process means we have made up our minds to rewrite our software, consciously.

The software is not by itself a problem. If it becomes the

ruling factor, then it becomes a problem. The software is good only if you have some freedom from it. The moment you perform actions with your life energies instead of your body, intellect or emotion, you can suddenly move to a new level of freedom within yourself and outside of yourself. I have seen any number of people who start doing a simple kriya, and suddenly become so creative that they start doing things that they never imagined possible in their life. This is simply because they loosened their karmic foundations a little; they shook up their life energies for a change, instead of doing things with just their body, intellect or emotion. This is something every human being can learn to do.

THE NEXT STEP

Life goes on naturally according to a certain law. If you know the nature of life within you, if you understand this law, you can completely take charge of the way life happens. Right now, your destiny is written by you unconsciously. If you have mastery over your physical body, fifteen to twenty per cent of your life and destiny will be in your hands. If you have mastery over your mind, fifty to sixty per cent of your life and destiny will be in your hands. If you have mastery over your life energies, one hundred per cent of your life and destiny will be in your hands.

Body Blueprint

'You can play with life whichever way you want, but life cannot leave a single scratch upon you. Every human being is capable of living like this.'

As there is a medical physiology, there is a whole yogic physiology. In yoga, we look at the body as five sheaths or five layers.

The first layer of body, *annamaya kosha*, is called the food body. What you call 'body' right now is just an accumulated heap of food.

The second layer, the *manomaya kosha*, is the mental body. Today doctors are telling you that you are a 'psycho-soma'– this means that whatever happens in the mind happens in the body. This is simply because what you call 'mind' is not just in any one place; every cell has its own intelligence, so there is a whole mental body. Whatever happens in the mental body happens to the physical body, and in turn, whatever happens in the physical body happens in the mental body. Every fluctuation on the level of the mind has a chemical reaction, and every chemical reaction in turn generates a fluctuation on the level of the mind. Because of this, an extensive manifestation of psychosomatic ailments has happened.

The physical body and mental body are like your hardware and software. Hardware and software cannot do anything unless you plug into quality power, isn't it? So the third layer of the body is *pranamaya kosha,* or the energy body. If you keep your energy body in perfect balance and fully activated, there can be no such thing as disease either in your physical body or in your mental body.

When I say 'disease', I am only talking about chronic ailments, not infectious diseases. Infectious diseases happen because of external organisms, but human beings are every day manufacturing their own diseases. Once your energy body is in full vibrancy and proper balance, disease cannot exist in the physical body. Whatever the disease there, it manifests itself because, for some reason, energy is not functioning the way it should.

> The physical body and mental body are like your hardware and software.

I can show you thousands of people who have gotten rid of their physical ailments or even psychological problems just by doing certain simple yogic practices. Now these practices are not aimed at the disease. The practice is just aimed at bringing proper vibrancy and balance in your energy body. If you handle your pranamaya kosha properly, physical wellness is naturally taken care of. Other dimensions also become available to you as the pranamaya kosha becomes more subtle and accessible. There are yogic processes through which you can exercise your energy body.

These three dimensions of the body – annamaya kosha, manomaya kosha and pranamaya kosha – are physical in existence. Take the example of a light bulb; it is physical. The electricity behind it is also physical, but subtler. You cannot see it; well, if you stick your finger in a light socket, you can feel it! The light that is emanating from the bulb is also physical but much subtler. The bulb, the electricity, the light – all these three are physical. One, you can hold in your hand; another, you can feel; and of course, another takes a much more sensitive receptor, like the eye, to know it. You can experience all these things because you have the sense perceptions to experience them. But you have no other perception to experience that which is beyond the physical.

The fourth layer is the *vignanamaya kosha*, or the etheric body. Vignanamaya is a transient state. It is neither physical nor non-physical; it is like a link between the two. It is not in your current level of experience, because your experience is limited to the five sense organs.

The fifth layer, the *anandamaya kosha*, is beyond the physical. '*Ananda*' means 'bliss'. It has nothing to do with the physical realms of life. A dimension which is beyond the physical cannot be described or defined, so we talk about it in terms of experience. When we are in touch with that aspect which is beyond the physical, which is the source of everything that we are, we become blissful. With reference to our experience, we call it the bliss body. It is not that you are walking around with a bubble of bliss inside of you. It is just that when you touch this dimension which is non-physical in nature, which can be neither described nor defined, it produces an overwhelming sense of bliss. This is why it is termed the bliss body.

These are the five layers of the body. If the physical, mental and energy bodies – the annamaya kosha, manomaya kosha and pranamaya kosha – are perfectly aligned you will find access to the bliss body. This innermost non-physical nature will find expression by pervading the three surface layers.

When it comes to external realities, each one of us is differently capable. What one does the other may not be capable of doing, but when it comes to inner realities, all of us are equally capable. Every human being is capable of experiencing life in a blissful manner. There is no certainty as to whether you can sing, dance, climb a peak or make money. But making your life experience a blissful experience of utmost pleasantness and harmony cannot be denied to you, if you are willing. Your journey through life becomes absolutely effortless and to the fullest potential without any stress or strain. You can play with life whichever way you want, but life cannot leave a single scratch upon you.

The Mystic Sage

'**Agastya did not use any other substance as a spiritual tool, except the body, the breath, and the energy. It was just *this* piece of life that he worked with. This is unique.**'

In the yogic tradition, Shiva is not seen as a God, but as the first yogi, the Adiyogi. After thousands of years, the spine of knowledge that Adiyogi created is still the source of almost everything that you can call spiritual on the planet. He transmitted this knowledge of the human mechanism to the seven celebrated sages who were his direct disciples, generally known in India as the *Saptarishis*, whom he sent to different corners of the world.

Agastya, often considered to be the foremost of these sages, covered the Indian subcontinent. Almost any place you go in this country, there are legends about him. If you look at the volume of work that he did, and consider the distances that he covered by foot, he must have lived an extraordinary span of time. They say it took him four thousand years of work to accomplish all that he did. We do not know whether it is four thousand or four hundred, but he definitely did live for a remarkable length of time.

He established hundreds of ashrams around the country, with the aim of making spirituality a part of everyday life. The energy and the wisdom with which he handled everything are quite superhuman. They say he did not spare a single human habitation in the subcontinent. You can still find the remnants of his work in every family in this country, families who are unknowingly doing some kind of yoga in diluted forms. If you look carefully, the way they sit, the way they eat, whatever is being done traditionally, is the remnant of Agastya's work.

Agastya is considered the father of South Indian mysticism. There are various mystical processes on the planet, but South Indian mysticism is unique in its nature. The mystics who came here were not persecuted; as a result, they could explore and experiment whichever way they wanted. Unfortunately, most mystics have not had this sort of conducive atmosphere in other parts of the world. So South Indian mysticism grew in such intricacy and profoundness that it is unmatched anywhere else on the planet. It is unique for its absence of ritual and its phenomenal methods of using the human system towards the exploration of the unknown.

One significant difference between the other systems and Agastya's is that other systems use multiple objects and rituals to enhance their spirituality. But Agastya did not use any substance as a spiritual tool other than the body, the breath, and the energy. It was just *this* piece of life that he worked with. This is unique.

Agastya mastered the ways of kriya, and wherever he went, he established the ways of this most powerful path of yoga. Kriya means an inner action through which you can dismantle this life completely and put it back together again. Today anybody who belongs to any kind of kriya tradition will acknowledge Agastya Muni as its ultimate exponent.

In terms of bringing the spiritual process into practical life, not as a teaching, a philosophy, or a practice, but as life itself, just a few yogis managed to quietly transform the landscape. Agastya Muni was the most effective.

Kriya: The Classic Action

'If you want the kriya to be a live process, to be imprinted in your system in a certain way, then it needs a certain discipline and dedication.'

Fundamentally, '*kriya*' means 'internal action.' When you do inner action, it does not involve the body and the mind because both the body and the mind are still external to you. When you have mastery enough to do inner action with your energy, then it is a kriya.

Kriya yoga is a very powerful way to walk the spiritual path, but at the same time it is very rigorous. What it demands out of a person is tremendous. For today's educated people, not accustomed to using their body in its full versatility, kriya yoga would be inhuman because it needs a certain kind of discipline and exactitude. Most people don't have the body, the intellect or the stability of emotion for the kriya yoga path any more, because right from childhood, people are in too much comfort. I don't mean just physical comfort. Sitting in a comfortable chair is not an obstruction. But you are seeking comfort always: this is a great obstruction. If you are sitting on something which is comfortable, enjoy it – there is no problem about it. But if you are constantly seeking comfort, then that kind of mind and emotion is unsuitable for the path of kriya. Kriya yoga cannot be done with people who talk 'freedom' all the time. It is not for people who keep asking, 'Am I not free to do this? Am I not free to do that? Why can't I eat this? Why can't I sleep there?'

If you take the path of kriya, and you are told to sleep with your legs up and head down, that is exactly what you should do, without asking questions, because all of it can never be explained. You may understand as you go along, but it can never be explained. And if it has to be explained, the essence of the kriya will be lost. If people start asking logical questions about everything, obviously logical correct answers must be given, but kriya is a tool to transcend the framework of logic and imbibe dimensions which are considered mystical.

If we want to teach you kriyas just as practices, I can write a book about them, and you can read and learn them. But if you want the kriya to be a live process, to be imprinted in your system in a certain way, then it needs a certain discipline, dedication and trust. When you walk a completely new terrain, if there is no trust in the one who guides you, then the journey could become unnecessarily long and difficult.

Generally on the path of kriya, most gurus make the disciples wait. Suppose you go to a guru and you want to learn kriya yoga, he might say, 'Okay, sweep the floor.'

'No, I want to learn kriya yoga.'

'That is why I said, sweep the floor.'

You swept the floor for one year and said, 'I did one year of sweeping.'

'Oh, you are done with one year of sweeping the floor? Wash the dishes.'

The guru will just make him wait and wait. If still his trust does not waver, then perhaps he can be initiated into the kriyas. Otherwise, once you empower a person in a particular way such that his system is vibrant beyond normal standards, if his attitudes and emotions are not as they should be, he will cause immense damage to himself. But in today's world, to get that kind of time with people, to make them wait, to come to that kind of trust and then imprint these kriyas – it is not impossible, but the chances are remote.

Kriya yoga is important only if you want to do things beyond self-realization. If your interest is only to somehow escape this prison, if you just want enlightenment or *mukti*, then you don't really have to walk the kriya yoga path. If you just want to be liberated, kriya as a full-fledged path is not necessary because it needs too much application, discipline and focus. You can use kriyas in a small way; they need not be too intense.

If you follow the path of kriya very intensely without guidance, it may take a few lifetimes to bear fruit. If there is somebody here who can actively participate in and guide the process, then kriya can be a most powerful and magnificent way to explore the inner nature and mystical phenomena. Otherwise kriya is a somewhat roundabout way. What you are seeking on this path is not just realization; you also want to know the mechanics of life-making; you want to know the engineering of life. That is why it is a much longer process.

People who are on the kriya path have a completely different kind of presence about them because of their mastery over their energies. They can dismantle life and put it back together. If you are pursuing other ways, like gnana for example, you could become razor-

> People who are on the kriya path have a completely different kind of presence about them because of the mastery over their energies.

sharp. You can do many things with your intellect, but still there is nothing much you can do with your energy. If you are on the bhakti path or path of devotion, there is nothing much you can do with your energies, and you don't care because the sweetness and the focus of your emotions is all that matters; you only want to dissolve. If you are on the path of karma, you do many things in the world, but you can do nothing with yourself. But kriya yogis can do whatever they wish with themselves in terms of energy, and they can do a lot with the world as well.

Women and Kriya

'If one wants to progress on the spiritual path, it is always best to mix all aspects of life and create a proper combination of the four dimensions of gnana, karma, kriya and bhakti.'

Traditionally, it has been believed that kriya yoga is only for men. This is not because the yoga is of that nature, but because social conditions in the past were of that nature. Kriya yoga also involved being away from the normal situations of life which, traditionally, was not possible in this culture for a woman, because by the time she was eight or nine years of age, she was married. By the time she was fifteen, she usually had a child. Also, all the kriya yoga practices that were designed and structured by various masters were male-oriented because their disciples were male. This does not mean that no woman walked the kriya yoga path. Several women did, but they were a minority and so not too many practices were designed for them.

Yes, a woman can walk the kriya yoga path, but if she wants to walk it a 100 per cent , she is slightly disadvantaged, biologically. She has a small inherent handicap so she needs to put in a little extra effort.

But in any case, if one wants to progress on the spiritual path, it is always best to mix all aspects of life and create a proper combination of the four dimensions of gnana, karma, kriya and bhakti. Generally, in women, the emotional dimension is more dominant than the other dimensions, so it is good to make use of that. I have found that if a woman seeker has a little bit of bhakti in her, then her kriyas just get fired up so easily. This is not 100 per cent true with every man or woman, but what you refer to as masculine is more comfortable with a combination of gnana, kriya and karma, while the feminine is more comfortable with bhakti and kriya as a combination.

Labyrinth of Life

'Any experience that happens within you is just a certain expression of your life energies.'

There are 72,000 *nadi*s or channels in the human energy body. The energy moves through these channels. These 72,000 nadis spring from three basic nadis: the right is known as *pingala*, the left is known as *ida* and the central is known as *sushumna*.

These three nadis are the basis or the backbone of the energy system. Pingala is symbolized as the masculine. Ida is symbolized as the feminine. When I say 'masculine' and 'feminine', it is not in terms of gender, but certain aspects of nature. Certain qualities in nature have been identified as masculine, and certain other qualities as feminine. These qualities are represented by these two channels.

If your pingala is very pronounced, then the masculine, the outgoing, aggressive qualities, will be dominant. If the ida is more pronounced, the feminine, the receptive and reflective qualities, will be dominant. Your being a man or a woman has nothing to do with this; you may be a man, but the ida may be more dominant; you may be a woman, but the pingala may be more dominant.

The pingala and ida are also symbolized as the sun and the moon – the sun representing the masculine, and moon representing the feminine. The sun is aggressive and outgoing. The moon is reflective, and its cycles are connected with the feminine body as well. On the level of your mind, pingala represents the logical dimension; ida represents the intuitive dimension. These two dualities are the fundamentals of the physical sphere of life. A human being is complete only when both the masculine and the feminine function at full force and are in proper balance.

Sushumna, the central nadi, is the most significant aspect of your physiology, which generally goes unexplored. Sushumna is independent of this whole system, but it is the fulcrum for the whole system. Once the energies enter your sushumna, irrespective of what is happening around you, you have a certain balance. Right now, you may be reasonably balanced, but if the outside situation goes haywire, you will also go haywire. Once energies enter into sushumna, however, your inner way of being becomes independent of the outside.

The nadis do not have a physical manifestation. If you cut the body and look inside, you will not find them. But as you become more and more aware, you will notice the energy is not moving at random but in established pathways. *Chakras* are powerful centres in the physiology where the nadis meet in a particular way to create an energy vortex. Like the nadis, the chakras are of a subtle nature and do not have a physical existence. They always meet in the form of a triangle (not circles), but we call them chakras, because they suggest movement,

> As you become more and more aware, you will notice that the energy is not moving at random but in established pathways.

dynamism. '*Chakra*' means a 'wheel'. Every moving part in every machine is always a circle, as a circle is capable of movement with least resistance.

There are 114 chakras in the body, but generally we talk about the seven important chakras which represent the seven dimensions of life. The seven fundamental chakras are: *muladhara*, which is located at the perineum, the space between the anal outlet and the genital organ; *swadhishthana*, which is just above the genital organ; *manipuraka*, which is just below the navel; *anahata*, which is just beneath the centre of the rib cage; *vishuddhi*, which is at the pit of the throat; *agna*, which is between the eyebrows; and *sahasrar*, also known as the *brahmarandra*, which is at the top of the head (the fontanelle, where newborn infants have a soft spot).

Experiences that happen within you – anger, misery, peace, joy and ecstasy – are different levels of expression of your life energies. The chakras are the seven different dimensions through which one's energies find expression. If your energies are dominant in muladhara, then food and sleep will be the most dominant factors in your life. If your energies are dominant in swadhishthana, pleasure will be most dominant in your life; this means you enjoy physical reality in many ways. If your energies are dominant in manipuraka, you are a doer; you can do many things in the world. If your energies are dominant in anahata, you are a very creative person. If your energies are dominant in vishuddhi, you become very powerful. If your energies are dominant in agna, then you are intellectually realized. Experientially, it has not happened yet, but intellectual realization brings you to a certain state of peace and stability within yourself, irrespective of what is happening outside of you.

These are just different levels of intensity. A pleasure-seeker has more intensity to his life than someone whose life is just food and sleep. The man who wants to initiate something in the world has much more intensity than a pleasure-seeker. An artist or a creative person lives his life more intensely compared to these three people. If you move into vishuddhi, it is a completely different dimension of intensity and agna is much higher still. If you hit your sahasrar, you will explode into unexplained ecstasies. Without any external stimulant or reason, you are simply ecstatic because energies have touched a certain peak.

THE NEXT STEP

The very way the karmic structure works in every human being is essentially cyclical. If you observe very closely, within a day the same cycles are happening many times over. If you are very observant, you will see that every forty minutes you are going through a physiological cycle. Once you see that every forty minutes you are going through a certain cycle over and over again, with the necessary attention and awareness you can ride the cycle and move towards transcendence from the limitations that these cycles set. So, every forty minutes, life presents you with an opportunity – the opportunity to become conscious.

Every forty to forty-eight minutes, there is also a shift of dominance in the way the breath is moving through the right and left nostrils. It is dominant in the right nostril for a length of time, and then in the left. Become aware of this so you know at least something about you is changing. This awareness can be further enhanced into awareness of the solar and lunar influences upon the body. There are specific tools that one can be offered if a certain fundamental sense of awareness is achieved. If you bring your physical system into sync with the lunar and solar cycles, your physical and psychological health is guaranteed.

Sacred Science

'If you have the necessary technology, you can make the simple space around you into a divine exuberance; you can just take a piece of rock and make it into a god or a goddess.'

Consecration is a live process. The Sanskrit word for it is *'pratishtha.'*

If you transform mud into food, we call this agriculture; if you make food into flesh and bone, we call this digestion; if you make flesh into mud, we call this cremation; if you can make this flesh or even a stone or an empty space into a divine possibility that is consecration.

If, as modern science tells us, everything is just the same energy manifesting itself variously, what you call the divine, what you call a stone, what you call a man or a woman, or a demon, are all the same energy functioning in different ways.

For example, the same electricity becomes light or sound or something else, depending upon the technology. If you have the necessary technology, you can make the simple space around you into a divine exuberance; you can just take a piece of rock and make it into a god or a goddess. This is the phenomenon of consecration.

An enormous amount of knowledge about this dimension of life was perpetuated particularly in the Indian culture. It was recognized here that at some point, every human being will want to get in touch with the source of creation. If that possibility is not created across the planet and made available to every individual who seeks, then society has failed to provide true well being for a human being. It is because of this awareness that, in this culture, they built numerous temples on every street. The logic was that even a few metres should not pass without the presence of a consecrated space. The idea was not to create one temple rivalling the other. The idea was simply that no one should live in a space which is not consecrated.

It is a fortune for a human being to be in a consecrated space; the very way he lives becomes distinctly different. You may ask, 'Can't I live without it?' You can. For one who knows how to make his very body into a temple, going to the temple is not so significant. Yes, you can consecrate your own body. But the question is, are you able to keep it that way?

Spiritual initiations have all been towards consecrating this flesh into a temple-like space; after that, all that is needed is maintenance. Doing sadhana every day is one way of trying to maintain the body so that it is fit enough for the initiation processes that one has been through. I have given powerful

> The very basic purpose of building a temple is particularly to benefit those people who have no sadhana in their life.

consecrations to people at various times, sometimes formally, sometimes informally. To consecrate an inanimate object – a rock, for example—costs an enormous amount of life. Making human beings into living temples is much more inexpensive and eco-friendly – and besides, they are mobile! There are many advantages, but the problem is human beings have to dedicate a certain amount of time, energy, resource and focus towards that; otherwise it will not work.

When people in the world are too distracted, when they are unwilling to work to make themselves into living temples, building stone temples becomes a necessity. The very basic purpose of building a temple is particularly to benefit the majority of people who have no sadhana in their life. If one can do sadhana in that space, it is doubly beneficial. Particularly for one who does not know how to make his own body into a temple, the outer temple is invaluable.

Pratishtha is done in various ways, but generally by using rituals, mantras, sounds, forms and various other ingredients. This means constant maintenance is required. Traditionally they tell you not to keep stone idols at home. If you do keep them, every day you must maintain them with the right kind of *puja* and other rituals. This is because if a deity is consecrated through mantras, and if the rituals and necessary maintenance work do not happen on a daily basis, the deity becomes a withdrawing energy and can cause immense harm to people who live in the vicinity. Unfortunately, many temples have become like this because of improper maintenance by people who do not know how to keep them alive.

Prana pratishtha is different in that it uses your own life energies to consecrate something. When you consecrate a form in this way, it does not need any maintenance; it is forever. That is the reason why there are no rituals and pujas for the Dhyanalinga meditation shrine in Coimbatore; it does not need any. The rituals in most temples are not for the devotee's sake; they are to keep the deity alive. But the Dhyanalinga does not need that maintenance; it will never fluctuate. Even if you take away the stone part of the *linga*, it will remain the same. Even if you destroy the planet, the energy form of the linga will not perish. This is because the real linga is made of a non-physical dimension. You cannot destroy it.

Wherever you spend most of your time – your home, your street, your office -- those spaces should ideally be consecrated. Your inner evolution need not stick to the Darwinian scale; you can simply leapfrog ahead if you live in such a space. It is my dream that some day all of humanity should live in consecrated spaces.

THE NEXT STEP

The temples in India were never places of prayer. The tradition is that first thing in the morning you have a bath, go to the temple,

*sit there for a while, and only then begin your day. The temple was
like a public battery-charging space.*

*Most people have forgotten this these days; they just go to
temples, ask for something, just touch their bottom to the floor
and come out. That is not the point of these spaces. The idea is to
go and imbibe their energies.*

*For example, we have the Dhyanalinga in Coimbatore. You
don't have to believe anything, pray, or offer anything there. You
just close your eyes and sit there for some time. Try it. It can become
a phenomenal experience. The Dhyanalinga is in the highest level of
intensity that any form can be. If even a person who doesn't know
anything about meditation comes and sits there, he will become
meditative naturally. That is the kind of tool it is.*

First and Final Form

'The temple is a hole in the fabric of the physical through which you could fall easily and go beyond.'

In this country, the temple was traditionally regarded as a place for you to go and dissolve yourself. It was only later when people started focusing on immediate well being that other temples came up.

Most ancient temples were built for Shiva, or 'that which is not'. There are thousands of Shiva temples in the country, and most of them do not have any idol as such; they generally have a representative form, a *linga*.

The word 'linga' means 'the form'. When the un-manifest began to manifest itself, or in other words when creation began to happen, the first form that it took was that of an ellipsoid, which is what we call a linga. It always started as a linga, and then became many other things. If you go into deep states of meditativeness, before a point of absolute dissolution comes, once again the energy takes the form of a linga. Modern cosmologists have identified that the core of every galaxy is always an ellipsoid, a three-dimensional ellipse. If you look within yourself, the very core form of you is also a linga. Generally in yoga, the linga is considered as a perfect form, the fundamental form of existence.

The first form and the final form is a linga; the in-between space is creation; and what is beyond is Shiva. So, the form of a linga is a hole in the fabric of creation. For physical creation, the back door is a linga, and the front door is a linga. This makes the temple a hole in the fabric of the physical through which you could fall easily and go beyond.

The science of linga-making is highly sophisticated. If a linga is made with the right kind of material and energized, it becomes a perennial storehouse of energy. In India many lingas have been created by siddhas and yogis for specific purposes with specific qualities.

As kings funded most of the temples, most lingas are of manipuraka nature. But a few kings who looked beyond that aspect of life wanted anahata lingas, or atma lingas, for love and devotion and ultimate dissolution. Anahata is a very malleable kind of state, accessible to most people. There are also muladhara lingas, which are very base, gross, and powerful, used for occult purposes.

> In yoga, the linga is considered as a perfect form, the fundamental form of existence.

Most of the lingas in the country right now represent one chakra or two at the most. The uniqueness of the Dhyanalinga is it has all the seven chakras energized at their peak. To create seven separate lingas for seven chakras would be so much

> The uniqueness of the Dhyanalinga is it has all the seven chakras energized at their peak.

easier, but the impact would not be the same. The Dhyanalinga is like the energy body of the most evolved being (traditionally referred to as Shiva). It is the highest possible manifestation. If you push up energy to very high levels of intensity, it can hold form only until a certain point. Beyond that, it becomes formless and people are incapable of experiencing it. The Dhyanalinga has been consecrated in such a way that the energy has been crystallized at the highest point beyond which there will be no form. It was created to allow a seeker the intimacy of sitting with a live guru. It is a rare opportunity.

It took three and a half years of a very intense process of consecration to complete the Dhyanalinga. Many yogis and siddhas have attempted to create such a form, but for various reasons, all the required ingredients never came together. Three lifetimes have been devoted towards fulfilling this. With the grace of my Guru and the support of several others, today, after a saga of three lifetimes, the Dhyanalinga stands complete, in all its glory.

The Dhyanalinga is a possibility to know and experience life in its utmost depth and totality. One who comes into its sphere is influenced on the level of the etheric body, or vignanamaya kosha. If you bring about a certain transformation through the physical, mental or energy body, it can be lost in the course of life. But once a person is touched on the level of his etheric body, it is forever. Even if he goes through many lifetimes, this seed of liberation will wait for the right opportunity to sprout and flower.

Drop of Ecstasy

'When you are aspiring to purify yourself, the rudraksh can be a support.'

The rudraksh is a seed from a particular tree which grows at a certain altitude, mainly in the Himalayan region. The word '*rudraksh*' comes from 'Rudra', which means Shiva, and 'aksha', which means teardrop.

One day Shiva sat in meditation and did not open his eyes for many millennia. He soared into such states of ecstatic meditation that he could not control his ecstasy. Tears of ecstasy fell and as they dropped upon this planet, they became rudraksh seeds. (That is the story. It is not a fact, but it is a truth. These myths and legends were created to express those dimensions of life which do not fit into the logical realm of understanding.)

Every substance has different kinds of vibrations, but the rudraksh has very unique vibrations and has a certain impact on the system. It is generally worn as a *mala* (a strand or necklace). One reason the rudraksh is worn on the body is to cleanse the aura, which is a certain field of light and energy around every creature and inanimate object. These days the aura is being captured through Kirlian photography and recorded in so many different ways -- from a pitch-black aura to a pure white aura, and a million shades in between. You have probably seen paintings of saints or sages with white haloes around their heads. The artist is obviously trying to convey that these are pure beings. This does not mean that if you wear a rudraksh, you will suddenly have a halo glowing behind your head! But when you are aspiring to purify yourself, the rudraksh can be a support. For someone who wants to scale the peak of consciousness, any little assistance is valuable.

Another reason why people on the spiritual path always wore the rudraksh in India is because they were constantly travelling. When you are constantly eating and sleeping in different places, there is a possibility that your system will get destabilized. You may have noticed this with yourself. You may have gone to a new place, where even if you are very exhausted, somehow your body will not settle down and sleep. If the energy around is not conducive to your aura, your system will not settle down. The rudraksh gives you a cocoon of your own energy, so you can sleep undisturbed and insulated. A person who is constantly travelling often wears a rudraksh so that outside energies do not disturb him.

Apart from that, there are various other benefits: the rudraksh has a certain reverberation which relaxes the whole system. It lowers your blood pressure, calms your nerves, and changes the very way the system behaves. Today doctors in India are actually prescribing the rudraksh for hypertension and cardiac ailments.

There is a lot of deception around these beads in the market. Customarily, the genuine rudraksh is sourced through certain families that have been dealing with these seeds for centuries. For them, it is not just business, but a sacred duty. If you intend to buy it, make sure you buy or receive your rudraksh from an authentic source.

Mountains of Grace

'Gurus usually used mountain peaks to download their knowing, because there is the least disturbance, the least movement of human beings in such places.'

For most gurus, the problem has been that they could never share what they realized with people around them. To create another person to receive what you know is not easy. If you find even one person you are fortunate.

So, most yogis and mystics always downloaded their knowing in some place or the other. There are many wonderful places like this in India. Gurus usually used mountain peaks to download their knowing, because there is the least disturbance, the least movement of human beings in such places. Mount Kailash* is the place where the maximum amount of knowledge

---

* Located in western Tibet, this sacred mountain peak is an important pilgrimage destination.

> Kailash is the greatest mystical library on the planet.

has been stored for a very long time in energy form.

Kailash is the greatest mystical library on the planet. Almost all the religions of the East hold it as highly sacred. For Hindus, it is the ultimate, the abode of Shiva and Parvati. The Buddhists hold it sacred because three of their greatest Buddhas are said to be living there. The Jains believe that the first Teerthankara still lives there. The Bon religion, the original religion of Tibet, also considers it deeply sacred.

There are other places of enormous vibration where people have done certain sadhanas. Such spaces are innumerable in the Himalayas. A variety of mystics and yogis chose these mountains as their abode. When they lived there they naturally left a certain dimension of energy, and as a result, the Himalayas gathered a certain kind of aura.

For example, Kedarnath is just a small temple in the Himalayas. There is no deity there; it is just an outcrop of a rock. But it is one of the most powerful places in the world! If you strive to improve your receptivity and then visit a place like that, it will just blow you away. There are many places like that in the East, but the Himalayas have attracted the maximum number of people.

Kumara Parvat in the southern state of Karnataka is another example. '*Parvat*' means 'mountain'. 'Kumara' refers to Shiva's son, whose name was Kartikeya. It is said that he fought many battles, trying to transform the world, but when he realized the futility of this, he came to a place now called Kukke Subramanya. It is here that he washed his sword of its blood for the last time. He decided that even if he fought for a thousand years, he was not really going to change the world, that one violent solution would breed another ten problems. So he climbed up and just stood on top of the mountain. Normally when a yogi wants to leave his body, he will either sit down or lie down. But because he was such a warrior, Kartikeya stood up and exited his body standing.

If one can exit the physical form without damaging it, that is an indication of absolute mastery over the life process. This is generally referred to as *mahasamadhi* or 'glorious equanimity'.

When I went to Kumara Parvat many years ago, a little tent was set up for me. I wanted to sleep in it, but when I went in and tried to lie down, my body would involuntarily move into a standing posture, dismantling the tent. The whole night I was not able to sit; my body would only stand. That is when I started seeing what Kartikeya's life was all about. While we do not know the exact date, this episode definitely seems to have happened over 12-15,000 years ago. But what he left behind is still vibrantly alive.

The interesting thing is that Kartikeya himself was a great experiment. The story goes like this. There were six infants with radiant qualities. Parvati, Shiva's wife, saw this and thought if all these six wonderful qualities were embodied in one person, how wonderful it would be! So, she merged these six children into one. Even today Kartikeya is known as six-faced or *Shanmukhi*. If you go up this mountain, wherever you dig on the mountain top, every pebble you pick up will be six-faced. These stones are

> Wherever a person does something with his life energies, he creates a certain space and a certain possibility which cannot be erased by any event.

called *shanmukha linga*s. If you hold them in your hand, they are explosive! These few thousand years, his energy has just been reverberating, and the stones have slowly shaped themselves into six faces.

Wherever a person does something with his life energies, he creates a certain space and a certain possibility which cannot be erased by any event. This kind of work can never be wiped out. Anybody who has experimented even a little bit with the inner dimensions, their work and their presence is never gone.

For example, Gautama Buddha is supposed to have lived 2500 years ago, but as far as I am concerned, he *is* right now. Jesus is supposed to have lived 2000 years ago, but in my experience, he *is* right now as well. Once you create a certain volume of work with your life energies, it is for always; you cannot destroy it. If you work with your body, using your bone and muscle, that kind of work has a certain lifespan. If you use your mind and function in the world, the lifespan of that work is much longer. But if you function with your fundamental life energies, it is timeless.

Kailash of the South

'The Velliangiri Mountains are called the 'Kailash of the South' because the Adiyogi, Shiva, himself spent a little over three months upon these mountain peaks.'

Right from my infancy, there were always mountains in my eyes. Only when I was sixteen years old and discussed this with my friends (and they said, 'You're crazy! Where are the mountains?') did I realize nobody had mountains in their eyes except me. For some time I thought I should find out where they are, but then I ignored that idea.

Suppose there is a spot on your spectacles, you get used to it after a while. It was just like that. It was only much later when a whole flood of memory came back to me, and when I was looking for a place to establish the Dhyanalinga, that I started looking for that particular peak in my eyes.

I travelled everywhere. I made at least four trips on my motorcycle from Goa to Kanyakumari and back again. Somehow I believed they must be in the Western Ghats. On every road and mud track from the range of Karwar down to the Kerala border in Karnataka, I have probably ridden thousands of kilometres.

Then just by chance I came to a village outside Coimbatore. As I was driving down a bend, I saw the Seventh Hill of the Velliangiri Mountains – it was right there, the mountain that I had always been seeing since my childhood. And from that day they disappeared from my eyes.

The Velliangiri Mountains are called the 'Kailash of the

South' because Shiva, or the Adiyogi, himself spent a little over three months upon these mountain peaks. When he came here, he was not in his usual blissful mood; he was angry with himself (as he had failed to keep his word to a woman). He was intense and despondent, and that energy is still evident today; it produced a string of yogis through the tradition who were of the angry sort. They did sadhana here and acquired that quality. They were not angry about anything in particular – simply angry.

One yogi who was significant for us at Isha is Sadhguru Shri Brahma who lived in the early part of twentieth century. And above all, this mountain is very important for us because this is where my Guru left his body. This mountain is like a temple for us in this yogic tradition. It is a cascade of divinity, a cascade of Grace.

If you ask me, 'Which is the greatest mountain on the planet?' I will always reply, 'Velliangiri', because for me these are not just mountains. I was born with an imprint of these mountains in my eyes and they have haunted me since. They lived within me and have been my very own navigating system, my GPS. These mountains were not a pile of rocks for me; they were a reservoir of what I needed to know to create the Dhyanalinga.

Healing Sideshow

'Using your energies to heal another person is a very juvenile act.'

Energy healing systems of various kinds are gaining prominence today. I am often asked my views on them.

I believe there are far too many healers on the planet! I am not saying there is nothing at all to it, but ninety per cent of the time, it is deception. Ten per cent of the time, there *is* something to it.

Suppose someone sells nothing to you, then he is just a smart businessman; you are a little stupid, but no harm happens to you except financial loss. You have the pleasure of shopping, and he is doing business. But if he sells you something which causes you harm, that is worse than selling nothing to you. The ten per cent of the time when something does happen, that is when it is dangerous and unnecessary.

Today with modern medicine, you can handle almost all

infectious diseases. The use of any kind of medicine is an attempt to change the chemistry of the body. With any kind of drug or external input, there will always be some disturbance to the system. On one level, the medicine cures you of the disease, but on another level, it creates a kind of suffering. When it goes beyond a certain point, then you say the drug has had side effects. There is a price to pay, but it is needed because the disease is a bigger problem for you.

However, chronic ailments do not come to you from any external organism. Here, the disease is just on the surface, like the proverbial 'tip of the iceberg'. The real problem is elsewhere within you.

In other words, the symptoms are like indicators. Whenever somebody attempts any healing, they are always trying to remove the symptom, because that is what they consider to be the disease. If you take away the indicator, the root of the problem still exists. The indicator manifested itself on the physical body just to bring that root to your notice. Instead of taking notice and seeing what should be done about it, if you just wipe out the indicator, the root will take effect in a much more drastic way in your system. What was asthma can become a big accident or some other calamity in your life. It is possible. If the root has to be removed, it has to be taken out and worked out in some way. It cannot just be dissolved.

Using your energies to heal another person is a very juvenile act. In the process of healing, you can cause great distress and damage to your own life in so many ways. If it was just your life getting damaged and you don't mind – you just want to be useful to somebody else – that is fine. But in the process of healing someone, you are also causing damage to the other person. Because people have not understood and experienced life in any great depth, but only in the physical dimension, they believe that relieving a person of his physical pain at a particular moment is the greatest thing they can do. It is not so. It is understandable that once the pain of disease comes, you just want to be relieved; it does not matter how. But if you are beginning to experience life a little deeper than the physical body, you will see that *how* you get rid of your disease also matters.

Disease will cease when you reorganize your own energies through sadhana. We are teaching kriyas to people where the objective is not healing, but healing anyway naturally happens. Just laying your hands on somebody and relieving him of pain is not a sensible way of handling disease.

Only people who live on the surface of life talk in terms of healing. If you have known any depth of life, you will not attempt any healing, nor will you seek any healing. You will see how to go beyond these limitations.

Another part of this whole activity of trying to heal somebody is that, in some way, you are trying to play God, trying to manipulate energies in a certain way. Getting instant relief will relieve you in one way, but bind you in some other way.

> Nobody who genuinely walks a spiritual path will ever attempt healing because it is a sure way of entanglement.

Nobody who genuinely walks a spiritual path will ever attempt healing because it is a sure way of entanglement. Some of the famous healing groups around the globe today were started by people who dropped out half-way through their spiritual process, after having acquired a little power. They wanted to use it and went on to market themselves well.

If you are on any live spiritual path, whoever is leading or guiding it will always make sure that you never acquire any kinds of power. We want to be very ordinary – *extra*-ordinary, in fact. We don't want the disease of trying to become 'special'. In trying to play God, in some way you want to do something that other human beings cannot do. This can lead to lots of entanglement. Most of the time, this healing business is a sideshow.

Technology for Transformation

'There is no guru without tantra.'

Today I see many phenomena associated with the occult sciences passing off as spiritual processes. Suppose I call you without using a phone, this is occult. Let us say I am in India and you are in America. I want to send a flower to you, but I am not willing to take the journey that Columbus took. If I make this flower suddenly land in your lap, this is occult. There is nothing spiritual about it; it is just another way of handling physical reality.

In India, we have sophisticated occult processes. There are people who can make your life or break your life just by sitting in one place in their homes. If someone just gives a picture of yours to one of them, they could look at you and see that tomorrow you get some freaky disease. Whatever the most bizarre disease in existence, he could let you have it tomorrow. These occult practitioners can also create health, but unfortunately most of them use their ability in other ways. Whether they produce ill health or good health, both are not advisable.

Have you heard of Gorakhnath? He was a disciple of Matsyendranath, a great yogi. In the yogic tradition, people do not make much distinction between Matsyendranath and Shiva himself, because they saw both were at about the same level of attainment. Many people worship Matsyendranath as nothing less than Shiva himself. They say Matsyendranath lived for about 600 years. Gorakhnath became his disciple, and he adored and worshipped his master.

Gorakhnath was all fire. Matsyendranath saw too much fire, and not enough sense. Fire burns through many things, so Gorakhnath started burning through the walls of ignorance, and suddenly he had enormous power. Matsyendranath saw that he was running a little ahead of himself, so he told him, 'Go away for fourteen years; don't stay near me. You are imbibing too much from me. Go.'

This was the hardest thing for Gorakhnath. If Matsyendranath had said, 'Give up your life,' he would have done it at once. 'Go away' he could not bear, but that was what was demanded of him, so he went away.

Fourteen years he counted the days, waiting for the day he could go back. The moment the period was over, he came rushing back. One of the disciple-yogis was guarding the cave where Matsyendranath stayed. Gorakhnath went to him and said, 'I want to see my master!'

The yogi who was guarding the cave said, 'I have no such instructions, so you had better wait.'

Gorakhnath flared up. He said, 'I've waited for fourteen years, you fool! I don't know when you came here. Maybe you came here day before yesterday. How dare you stop *me*!'

> Generally on the spiritual path, the occult is shunned completely.

He pushed him aside and went into the cave. Matsyendranath was not there. Then he came back and shook the disciple. He said, 'Where is he? I want to see my master now!'

The disciple said, 'I have no instructions to tell you that.'

Gorakhnath could not contain himself; he used his occult powers. He looked into the disciple's mind and found out where Matsyendranath was. He then started heading in that direction. His guru was waiting for him halfway.

Matsyendranath said, 'I sent you away for fourteen years, because you were beginning to become occult-oriented. You were losing your spiritual process and beginning to enjoy the power that it gave you. When you come back the first thing that you do is use the occult to open up my disciple's mind. Another fourteen years for you.' And so he sent him away again.

There are many stories about Gorakhnath jumping into this forbidden area, and Matsyendranath punishing him again and again. At the same time, Gorakhnath evolved into the greatest disciple that Matsyendranath ever produced.

This is how we always treated the occult in this culture. We did not treat it with respect, we did not treat it as valuable; we always saw it as a way of misusing life, intruding into

> Tantra is a certain
> capability; without it
> there is no spiritual
> process.

areas where you should not. Only certain types of people who are after power, money, or who are ruled by greed, practise the occult. Otherwise, in India, all these healings and related phenomena have been frowned upon. The attitude has always been such that if you get a disease, you see how to get well; if you don't get well, this is your karma and you live with as much equanimity as you can. When your time comes, you die consciously and try to attain liberation. But this desperation to somehow live at any cost stems from a certain ignorance.

The occult is not always a dirty thing, but unfortunately, it has earned this reputation. The occult is essentially a technology. No science or technology is intrinsically dirty. If we start using technology to kill or torture people, then after some time we think, enough of this damn technology! That is what has happened to the occult; too many people misused it for personal reasons. So, generally on the spiritual path, the occult is shunned completely.

What is often referred to as the occult is broadly *tantra*. In the current understanding in society, tantra is about using very unorthodox or socially unacceptable methods. But in its classical sense, *tantra* means 'technology'. There is a clear distinction between the occult kind of tantra and spiritual tantra. These two were classified as left-hand tantra and right-hand tantra and are completely different in nature.

Left-hand tantra involves various rituals which may seem

weirder than weird to many. Left-hand tantra is very external; you need materials and elaborate arrangements. Occult practices generally got referred to as the left hand of tantra, which gave people powers to communicate across distances, powers to appear in two different places at the same time, and use energies to their own benefit and to the detriment of others. Right-hand tantra is more internal; it is about enabling you to use your energies to make things happen. You use all the simple aspects of life as a subjective science to turn inward and do something with yourself. Left-hand tantra is a cruder technology. Right-hand tantra is a very refined technology. The question is what kind of tantra are you doing – low technology or high technology? If you want to make your energies move, do you have to do 10,000 rituals or can you just sit here and do that? That is the big difference.

Tantra is a certain capability; without it there is no spiritual process. If you have no tantra in you, you have no technology to transform people; all you have are words. Without a technology for transformation there is no master; so there is no guru without tantra. Today there are too many people claiming to be gurus but they are only rehashing scraps of paper from scriptures. A scholar cannot be labelled a guru. If there is no tantra in him, you cannot call him a guru.

Serpent Power

'The unmanifest energy of kundalini and a cobra have many similarities in their pattern of behaviour, hence the symbolism.'

The word '*kundalini*' literally means 'energy'. It is a certain type of energy within you which is untapped, un-aroused. The kundalini has always been symbolized in the yogic tradition as a coiled snake.

A coiled snake knows stillness of a very high quality – these coils hold a hidden volatile dynamism within themselves. When the snake is still, it is so absolutely still that even if it is lying right in front of you, you will miss it. Only when it moves, you see it. So kundalini is referred to as a coiled snake because this tremendous energy exists within you, but until it moves, you never realize it is there.

You would have noticed there is not a single Indian temple where there is no image of a snake. There will always be at least one figure of a snake somewhere, just to indicate that the temple is a possibility of arousing the un-manifest energies within you. Though physically a snake is far from the human system, it is very close in terms of energy. If you see a cobra in the wild, you might find it coming into your hands without any resistance because its energies and yours are so close to each other. The moment fear wells up within you, the snake immediately senses it, and thinks it is danger. If there is no fear, the snake will come to you effortlessly.

The snake is particularly drawn to one who becomes meditative. In the tradition, it is always said that if a yogi is meditating in a place, there will be a snake somewhere nearby. This is because if your energies become still, the snake is naturally drawn to you.

Mundane to Magical

'All miracles, or what are known as miracles, are just a deeper access to life that some have enjoyed.'

People who read of yogis attaining samadhi states are often curious: what is samadhi? How important is it on the spiritual path? How is it related to well being, to bliss?

Samadhi is a certain state of equanimity in which the intellect goes beyond its normal function of discrimination. This, in turn, loosens one from one's physical body such that there is a space between what is you and your body.

There are various types of samadhis, which for the sake of understanding have been classified into eight types. Among these eight there are two broad categories: *savikalpa* (samadhis with attributes or qualities, that are very pleasant, blissful, and ecstatic); and *nirvikalpa* (samadhis that are beyond pleasant and unpleasant, without attributes or qualities). In the case of nirvikalpa samadhi, there is only a single-pointed contact with the body. The rest of the energy is loose and uninvolved with the body. These states are maintained for certain periods to help establish the distinction between you and the body.

Samadhi is a significant step in one's spiritual evolution, but it is still not the ultimate. Experiencing a certain type of samadhi does not mean you are released from existence. It is just a new level of experience. It is like when you were a child, you had one level of experience. Once you move into your adulthood, you have another level of experience. You experience the same things in a totally different way at different points in your life. Samadhis are just like this.

> Samadhi is a significant step in one's spiritual evolution, but it is still not the ultimate.

Some people may go into a certain level of samadhi and stay there for years because it is enjoyable. In this condition, there is no space or time, no bodily problems – the physical and psychological barriers have been broken to some extent. But this is only temporary; the moment they come out, once again they get hungry, they have to eat, sleep, etc.

Generally, compared to a man who is sober, a man who is slightly drunk has a different level of experience and exuberance, but still he has to come down at some point. All samadhis, I would say, are a way of getting high without any external chemicals. By going into these states, a new dimension opens up for you, but it does not leave you permanently transformed. You have not moved into another reality. In the same reality, your level of experience has deepened, but you have not become free in an ultimate sense.

Most realized beings never stayed in samadhi states. Gautama never sat and meditated for twelve years in one place. Many of his disciples – many Buddhist monks – went into very long meditations for years. But Gautama himself never did this because he must have seen it was not necessary for him. He practised and experienced all the eight kinds of samadhis before his enlightenment, and he discarded them. He said, 'This is not it.' He knew this was not going to take him to realization. Samadhi is just moving into a higher level of experience and it is possible that you will get caught up with it, because it is far more beautiful than the current reality.

If you have made realization the top priority in your life, then anything which does not take you one step closer is meaningless. Let us say you are climbing Mount Everest, you will not take one step sideways because every ounce of energy is needed to reach the peak. Now, if you have to transcend your own consciousness, you need every ounce of what you have and still it is not enough. You would not want to perform any action that would distract you from the main purpose.

Now what is this realization, you might wonder. After all, all that most people are looking for is health, well being, wealth, love, and success. To put it in a simplistic way, isn't it true that the more you know about your computer, the better you can use it? Isn't it true for every gadget or instrument that you use, that your ability to use that to its fullest extent is directly proportional to your knowledge about it? Is it not true that someone who is dextrous and is an expert can use even a simple instrument in a magical way? Have you seen someone riding on a piece of plastic they call a surfboard, doing incredible things? Just a piece of plastic and see what they can do.

The more profound your realization of this being that you call yourself, the more magical your life will be. In every culture, there have been people who did things that made others believe in miracles. All miracles, or what are known as miracles, are just a deeper access to life that some have enjoyed. That access can be available to everyone.

Uncharted Path

The sixth limb of yoga is referred to as *dhyana*, which is essentially about transcending the boundaries of one's physical and mental framework. Dhyana travelled to China along with the Buddhist monks and became *Chan*. Chan travelled through the Southeast Asian countries to Japan and became *Zen*, and found expression as a whole system of direct insight without an emphasis on doctrine. Zen is one spiritual path which has no scriptures, books, rules, or rigid practices – it is an uncharted path.

The first recorded moment of Zen happened with Mahakashyapa and the Buddha. Such a moment probably happened many times before, but it didn't become a spiritual path as such. Every evening, Gautama would give many lectures about various aspects of spirituality. People listened keenly, but there was one monk, Mahakashyapa, who never showed any interest in what was said. Gautama would never instruct him to do meditation or teach him any practices. Mahakashyapa simply sat under the tree all the time. Everyone thought he had no intelligence and was of no use; they made fun of him. One day, Gautama came with a flower in his hands. He kept looking at the flower. There was a big crowd there, and everyone was waiting to hear his lecture, but he kept looking at the flower. They were all wondering why he did not speak when suddenly Mahakashyapa started laughing. Then Gautama said, 'I have given to all of you whatever I can through words. What I cannot give in words I am giving to Mahakashyapa.' He gave the flower to him. That, many believe, is the beginning of Zen.

There was once a Zen master. Everyone respected him, but he never had any teaching to impart. He always carried a huge sack on his shoulders; this would contain many items, and some part of it would be sweets. Every town and village he went to, children would gather around him, and he would distribute sweets and leave. People asked for teachings, but he would just laugh and go. One day, a man who was known to be a Zen adept of great repute, came and met this master, wanting to really know whether he was in Zen or not. So he asked him, 'What is Zen?' Immediately, the master dropped the sack and stood straight. Then he asked, 'What is the goal of Zen?' The master picked up the sack on his shoulders and walked away.

This is what yoga is also about, that is what every spiritual sadhana is about. When you want to attain yoga or Zen, call it what you like, you have to drop your load, discard everything that is on the way, remain free, stand upright. It is important.

With your loads you may never do it. And what is the goal of yoga? Take on the whole load once again! And now it no longer feels like a load.

Lunar Dance

'For a spiritual *sadhaka* who is always using every means possible to move his energies upward, these two days are like a boon from nature.'

The full moon day and new moon day offer powerful possibilities for someone on the spiritual path. '*Amavasya*' means a 'new moon day' (or 'no-moon day'). Whenever something or somebody dear to you is absent, their presence always becomes more powerful. If a friend or a loved one passes away, you feel their presence so much more intensely after they are gone. When they are gone, the vacuum that they have left behind becomes more powerful than their presence itself. Similarly with the moon, her absence makes her more present than ever before.

On amavasya, the earth broods. A certain integration of the elements is happening, so the life process on the planet slows down. When a certain slow-down happens, you notice your body much more. When everything is going well and you are busy, you do not know what is happening with the body; the body is just you. If a little ailment happens, suddenly the body is an issue; you have to pay attention to it. Only when it is not doing well do you know: 'This is not me. This is just my body giving me trouble.' A clear distance arises between you and your body. One can easily become aware of what is 'you' and what is 'not you', and from there onwards, the journey from untruth to truth begins. Even for those who are completely unaware, there is a natural opportunity every month available on amavasya to become more aware.

Pournami, or the full moon day, is more conducive for a feminine energy, so it is made use of by women on the spiritual path. Amavasya, by contrast, is very raw. When everything is pitch-dark, it is like creation itself has dissolved. There is a tinge of the destroyer or obliteration of physicality in amavasya. For a masculine energy seeking well being, pournami can be made use of as well, but for all those seeking liberation or absolute dissolution, amavasya is a bigger possibility.

You may have heard that if people are a little mentally unbalanced, on pournami and amavasya this imbalance becomes more pronounced. Why is this so? The impact of the moon on our planet pulls everything upward. Even the very ocean is trying to rise, and your own blood is also responding to the moon. If you are a little mentally unbalanced, because of the excessive circulation in your brain on that day, you will become a little more unbalanced. If you are happy, you become happier. If you are unhappy, you become unhappier. You have heard that many people fall in love on the full moon night! Whatever is your quality, it gets a little enhanced on those days because the whole energy is being drawn upward. For a spiritual *sadhaka* who is always using every means possible to move his energies upward, these two days are a boon from nature.

The Next Step

The fourteenth day of every lunar month, the day before the new moon or amavasya, is Shivaratri. Of the twelve that occur in a calendar year, the one that occurs in February—March, in the lunar month of Magha, is called Mahashivaratri because it is the most powerful. Mahashivaratri is of great significance because on this night even those engrossed in their day-to-day life can reap great spiritual benefits by being receptive. On this night, the planetary positions are such that, in the northern hemisphere, there is a natural upsurge of energies in the spine that can be beneficial if you keep your spine erect and remain alert and aware. If you can stay awake with the intention, 'I want to evolve', this night can be a powerful possibility.

You can try this on every full moon and new moon day as well: for ten minutes before and after midnight, simply sit with an erect spine. Even the oceans are trying to reach the heavens on these days. You will see that something within you will rise too. May such a night become an exuberant awakening of who you are rather than just a night of wakefulness.

Moon and the Master

'Guru Poornima is significant because it was on this day that the seed of liberation was planted in human consciousness.'

Over 15,000 years ago, in the upper regions of the Himalayas, a yogi appeared. Nobody knew who he was, where he came from. He came and sat absolutely still. People gathered in huge numbers around him because his presence was quite extraordinary. They waited, hoping for a miracle. Nothing happened. He just sat, completely oblivious to what was around him. Except for a few tears of ecstasy that fell from his eyes, he showed no signs of life at all. Because no one knew who he was, they called him Adiyogi, the first yogi.

A tremendous miracle was quietly happening before them, but people missed it completely. They could not see that his sitting still for days and months on end was the real miracle. They were expecting firecrackers. They did not happen. Everyone left. Only seven hardcore ones hung on.

When his attention fell on these seven, they pleaded with him to share his experience with them. He dismissed them. 'This is not for people who are seeking entertainment. Go away.' When they persevered, he gave them a few preparatory steps and said, 'Do this for some time and we'll see.'

Days rolled into weeks, weeks into months, months into years. But his attention never fell upon them again. They continued to perform a variety of austerities to become deserving candidates. Then after eighty-four years, on a full moon night in June, his eyes fell upon them. He could not ignore them any more. For the next twenty-eight days, he observed them closely. He saw they had reached phenomenal levels of readiness. And so, on the next full moon, Adiyogi decided to become a teacher or guru. He turned south and began expounding to them the nature of life and its possibilities. For the first time in human history he declared that it is possible for a human being to evolve consciously. On that day which marks the beginning of the *Dakshinayana* – the first full moon night after the summer solstice – Adiyogi became the Adi Guru, the first guru. That day is called Guru Pournami.

Darwin talked of biological evolution about 200 years ago. Adiyogi talked of spiritual evolution more than 15,000 years ago. It was on that full moon day that a whole exploration of the mechanics of life unfolded on the planet. This was the day that humanity first realized that the limitations set by nature are not absolute. You can become whatever you want. Nature has set you free. From here onwards, you cannot evolve unconsciously; if you want to evolve, you have to do it consciously. For the first time, the idea entered the human mind that you can cross your natural barriers, your animality, and come to a completely different dimension of existence.

This full moon, which falls in the lunar month of Ashadha (June–July), is known as Guru Pournami. It is important to understand this has nothing to do with religion. This event occurred before the idea of religion entered the human mind. Guru Pournami is significant because it was on this day that the seed of liberation was planted in human consciousness.

Conclusion: The Way Out

'It is very important that something beyond the physical is a living force in everybody's life.'

Human beings live out their lives. Many of their dreams come true. But when the time to die comes, they don't seem to know why they exist.

In the last few years, I have seen a few people – people I have known for a long time – dying. This includes one of my aunts and a few others who were very dear to me when I was young. They were good people, and their lives worked out according to their dreams. Everything that they wanted worked out: their sons went to America, their daughters got married to the right men (strictly in accordance with the horoscopes), and the grandchildren were cute. But, when the last few years of their life came, when death was approaching, they were completely broken people. Nothing wrong had happened; it was just life coming to its natural conclusion. Everything that they wanted had come true and now it was time to go. But now they were completely lost human beings. This is simply because there was no spiritual element in their lives. All they knew in their lives was their physical body, their psychological makeup, their emotions, and the people and things around them, and suddenly all those things did not mean anything any more. They were in a state of pathetic confusion, deeply disturbed, simply because there was no other dimension to stand upon.

These people lived well but they died badly. This is because when the physical and the psychological began to fail, suddenly they had nothing to hang on to. The physical and psychological *will* fail: this is not a prediction; it is a guarantee. It is very important that something beyond the physical is a living reality for everybody before life comes to an end.

A simple spiritual process, which does not need too much commitment, intellect and practice, is needed. It is needed urgently. Even if people do not live blissfully, at least they must die peacefully. There is no human being who does not deserve this.

One thing we have to realize, as a generation, is that for the very first time in the history of humanity, we have the necessary resources, capability and technology to address every issue on the planet – of nourishment, health, education, well being, you name it. The only thing that is missing is human consciousness, and that is something that has not been worked at. Everything is in place but the human being is not in place. If human beings get into the right space within themselves, every other solution is right at hand. The whole effort is to raise human consciousness in such a way as to bring human beings to a state of inclusiveness, so that the possibility that we are does not pass us by as a generation.

The way out or a solution lies within us, and it is only in turning inward that we can truly create a world full of love, light and laughter. Let us make it happen.

An Offering

If this book resonated with you in any way, you might want to try its most practical next step: the Isha Kriya DVD. The Isha Kriya is the only kriya offered by Sadhguru that does not require any formal initiation. Entirely non-sectarian and unaffiliated to any faith, this is a simple, scientific and effective process aimed at human well being. Although you reach it at the very end of your journey as a reader, it is the very heart of this book. A significant transformational tool, it is easy to turn into a part of your daily life.

—**The Isha Editorial Team**